*"All women know themselves beautiful. All it needs is for the beauty to be called out of them. . . . All women know this, no matter how broken and brainwashed they are by the merchants touting the fairy-dolls: they know seriously and honestly where their beauty lies, as they know precisely, even lacking the experience, what true mating is."* —Anne Zoltan

**This, then, is the story of a woman's search for her own beauty, and for the sexual relationship that would at last release it. . . .**

"In the case of female sexual experience . . . there has been . . . very little candid discussion of sex from the woman's point of view. *Annie* certainly helps to fill the gap, and her candor is sufficient to make . . . males tremble a little at the thought of Woman unleashed. This is not quite a Frank Harris-type memoir—it is . . . much more readable—but it does belong to the genre."
—*R. E. L. Masters, author of* Mind Games *and Director of the Foundation for Mind Research*

D1413316

# ANNIE:

## The Female Experience

### Anne Zoltan

A DELL BOOK

Published by
**DELL PUBLISHING CO., INC.**
1 Dag Hammarskjold Plaza
New York, New York 10017
First published in Great Britain
by Spencer Brown & Co. Ltd., Cambridge

Dell ® TM 681510, Dell Publishing Co., Inc.
Reprinted by arrangement with
The Julian Press, Inc.
Printed in the United States of America
First Dell printing—June 1974

# Chapter 1

I was born and raised, with thousands of other sheep, in Australia.

Not in the open stretches of the country, in the wide and empty land, where the growing things and rhythms of the spaces might have sung me the songs the humans around me had forgotten. But in the town; in a tiny, shocked, concrete, Jewish vivarium; a crowded, humid culture-cage; kept from the flow of the other beings in the city by the vivarium walls, both prison and refuge, inside which was the only breathable air for my scuttled kind.

We were ghetto people still; prisoners in a psychological slum.

They kept me very clean. My guardians. Guarded me from dirt. From bugs. From contaminating experience.

In the earliest of my wars against them, I preserved a patch of neck unwashed, under my hair, for weeks.

"Nice girls don't scratch, Annie."

"Nice girls always keep their clothes on, Annie."

"Nice girls don't wrestle with little boys, Annie. That's how you get babies."

They had, after all, a special view of nice girls: squinting at them through windows; spotting them briefly in public places. Their lack of imagination was remarkable: surely it could have been turned to financial advantage? Instant Eliminations Inc. What you don't see don't exist? Nice girls are clean.

The literature I was fed confirmed my family's view. In story books, where kids something like me had adventures I visualized in glistening detail, no one peed; nor did they suffer from constipation, in spite of the fact that no one crapped either. Perhaps I *was* dirtier than ordinary people?

My family was disconnected.

In its passage across the ocean, its members had forgotten their heritage; in the hounding and splitting of their families they had let slip their accumulated knowledge, stored by preceding generations. So that now they huddled and hid, trying to look like those they saw around them; these the sole fixed cues of their existence; nor daring to poke their noses—good Jewish noses honed for centuries for smelling rats—too far out of the vivarium, in case their camouflage wasn't as good as they thought; in case by some miscalculation their adversaries turned out to have noses as good as their own.

They trained me to hide. And fed me up. Don't let the bones show. The nearest they ever got to the bone was in the possession of one friend, Hannah, who had eaten her way through three husbands. So, at least, was my decision on the matter. She ate everything in sight.

My aunt hastened to add, whenever the subject of Hannah came up: "But one *did* die." It was more manageable to regard her as someone who had exchanged husbands only *once*. I would watch Hannah, pecking pinkly, trying to discover her fascination. Fruitless. Was this something like a . . . shh . . . woman of the streets? My stepfather was afraid of her.

Lamb into sheep, my stepfather and aunt tended me carefully. There was food by the ovenful. What they knew, they applied faithfully. The young need to eat. But all other aspects of mothering and husbandry were absent, jettisoned by pillar and post on the long route out.

Fortunately for me, the energy of Australia hung unfingered over the top of the town; held netted in the tips of the trees; skeined across the clouds and oceans. It communicated with me, and with what was in me. I breathed in the clear air high above, clean of my aunt's petulance and my stepfather's nervousness.

On the ground, subject to the pull of the pavement and street, there sounded scarcely an answering note. Under my feet was arid, implacable dusty hardness. I felt alien. But above me was air and energy, and I gulped it. I myself was all energy, though learning to hide and protect myself from the depredations of others.

The energy remained, a lit fuse, undirected, inside.

So I grew up energetic and empty, my vitality untempered either by knowledge or wise judgment.

Curiously, sex never entered my mind much while I was a child. I read fairy stories, where enchanting or ravishing events took place, and I read love stories, where prince won princess in latitudes, and among vegetation, I had never seen. But naturally enough I never thought of connecting these marvels with the rude things runty Chicken Rothschild once tried to do to me with his water pistol, when we were six.

Only one other sexual event of the time stands out: Chicken and me watching two dogs—the male attempting to mount the arched and panting female. We stood absorbed, silent; then retired behind the house to try: but failed, for we kept our clothes on.

Few such memories remain. Perhaps the daylong sun and swimming bleached and washed them out; and perhaps the heat and water also consumed energies which might later have been directed toward masturbation (of which I had neither heard nor conceived), or sex games, or early coupling. ——

Or perhaps it was simply that there was a shroud over sex, as there was over so much else, laid there by my eunuchoid, androgynised guardians, ensuring that my agitated energies would never direct my thoughts toward my private parts. Pregnancy, I remember thinking, was an interesting disease which through some good fortune visited only the married. Sex differentiation, similarly, must have had something to do with the shape of the navel. I decided this scientifically, on the only available evidence: unfortunately there were never any clues visible below the line of the bathing trunks.

For the only time that I tried, Chicken refused to let me take his pants down, and he could run faster.

# Chapter 2

My first remembered "sex" was free-floating, non-specific. The idea that the sensation I felt was to do with "sex" never entered my mind until I was no longer a virgin. Then I looked back and put the name "sex" on this fleeting moment.

But now I think I was wrong.

I think that any spark lit between people in this particular way is not "sex." That is far too limiting a label. It is more like "communication"—a force along the energy lines, which is *always* so traveling, suddenly shorting by surfacing into consciousness.

What else could it have been when I, fourteen years old, lifted my head from the tea table where I was sitting, in a cafe with my parents, and encountered the gaze, over the heads of several others so that all I could see was his head, of a youngish man . . . a gaze without any meaning or intention in it in the commonplace sense that one can read the "expression." It was indifferent and open. And as our gaze met, I was swallowed into a sensation I would now call orgasm, though not a localized, genital-centered affair. It was a cloud of sensation building up through my body and being, holding my edges totally inside it; holding, and then blowing to fullness, and then cleanly going. A total sensation which was there one moment and not the next; I was entirely gripped while I was in it; entirely innocent of it when it was gone.

The next "sensation" was about a year later, when dancing with a friend of my stepbrother. I had been bouncing about happily with two or three other boys during the evening; but when this Leon touched me I trembled so violently, energy line running from toes to fingertips, that I would have fallen if he had not been holding me.

I pressed my body to his, and we danced cheek to cheek. I felt fused to him; seared like cloth to a too-hot iron, or meat to a red-hot skillet. I couldn't have pulled apart. I could hardly breathe. When the dance ended he thanked me, surprise in his face, and didn't come near me the rest of the evening. I was both hurt and relieved. These, after all, were big boys—eight years older; inappropriate—not inside my framework or context. I could excuse myself from consequences of contact with them. This event was an anomaly, and better left alone—though later, I am afraid, it was transformed into an aching, adolescent romantic dream and I clothed the sensation with a vehicle quite unlike Leon (except in appearance) and more like the romantic images of my time—strong, knowingly masculine, and so on.

Poor kid. He disappeared under the burden of it.

Another "sensation." A boy staying in the same holiday hotel. Whenever we spoke my whole musculature would collapse; I could hardly stand upright. All these intense "sensations" (I was like a moth to flame: no reference to the quality or style of the flame's container) were anomalies, in terms of social context; or of *any* day-to-day conscious context. And so I kept them: my private illuminated moments; the first beads on a secret thread; to be hidden away from anyone else's gaze and even from my own day-to-day awareness. Treasured; locked away; nothing to do with anyone (including those who had inspired and perhaps participated in them) but something to do with my search. Sex and love and romance and a man. Those were the parameters of my search.

I was a daughter of my time, after all: bred from childhood to adapt any real experience and real aspiration rigidly into these forms and labels.

Paradoxically, it was only years later that I learned that such "clear light" and infusing, obliterating sensations, had been misinterpreted by me (as by most others) and were an aspect of a quite different, or rather, less limited, kind of perception and communication; paradoxically, because I learned this lesson through sex itself. In doing so, I lost my real virginity—and gained the beginnings of true understanding. For although it was lovely, it was only my physical virginity I lost with Arne.

The rest of me slumbered on.

# Chapter 3

Arne was the first.

The sexual prohibition in my life had been total. DON'T was all I was told.

DON'T.

Nothing was described or amplified, for the words were too magical and destructive for my guardians to say. As a result, none of the boys of "my sort" could get near me, for in my mental map they were associated with my family and social group; part of the context inside which the only thing that loomed, sex-wise, was the black and fearsome DON'T.

And so much did I NOT, being dutiful and eager to please and softhearted and shit-scared of people's disapproval, that no thought of what it *was* that I shouldn't do ever broke through the barrier into conscious thought. All around me I heard girls giggling about boys, locating and estimating the effect of their touch, and I would withdraw and think high-and-mighty, unmeaty, idealistic thoughts about true love.

Whenever there was no chance of anything getting too near the nitty-gritty, I pretended and played roles. For as far as I was concerned the whole of life seemed some mysterious game of pretense I couldn't work out, and it was fortunate I was a good mimic and had a quick ear, and so could get by as if I was just like the rest. The fact that nobody noticed the difference made it absolutely clear to me that in fact it *was* some sort of game I hadn't been told about.

So I would pretend, remarkably successfully, taking my cue from others, daring in speech, big on delight (for I lived in a nimbus of energy and optimism) and quick to withdraw if real life started approaching. Real life demanded *me*. And I was sleeping somewhere. The mimic and clown was not equipped to deal with anything that would call out the *person*, me.

Which meant, in essence, that I would neck within given localities with some of the boys I knew, and run like a rabbit away from what or whom I considered to be a "real man."

I had these classifications ("controllable," "nice Jewish boy," and "the *real* thing—hide quickly") so firmly fixed in my head, so neatly categorized, that when I met Arne and he fitted none of these, produced no associations of any kind because he was so out of my social context and experience, I simply took him as he stood.

For once, things were allowed to take their course.

Arne wasn't a "boy" in my restricted meaning

of the word (because he came from another culture, the cues were missing) and it was easy to see that he wasn't yet a frightening grown man. With hindsight I can say that he was twenty, Swedish, had blue eyes, blonde hair, parents who were farmers, and was a fairly decent country boy in town to study.

We had coffees, cokes, flirtatious skirmishes.

We went for a walk once.

He took me to a cinema.

Then once he came to my room, I made coffee, and we started necking almost immediately. It was no better or worse than with anyone else. My boundary lines were fixed close in: neck up, OK; arms, fine; breasts as the last gift, but only outside the clothes. My attention was so fixed on patrolling the boundaries that I never had too much of it left to give over to enjoying myself. Lines of energy would flicker over the barriers to see if his hands were going too far or even were about to . . . I was always three moves ahead in this sexual chess . . . and I would do a lot of heavy breathing to make up for my almost total psychological absence from the scene.

So there was I, sending out my mental scouts to police the verboten bits, and there was Arne, straightforwardly proceeding from place to place, and perhaps it was because he was so outside my elders' prohibitions (they couldn't have prohibited this sort of boy because he was as much beyond their experience as mine) that I suddenly thought, as his hand moved downwards, oh well, why not.

So he got to my waist (which few had managed) and then proceeded downward. There was a little legstroking which I found so marvelous that I simply shifted gears into another dimension, floating easily toward the clouds and then above them in a creamy smooth rise. And then he tugged off my pants, and put his hand between the little lips.

Believe it or not, I didn't have a clue that this is what was "done." I didn't have a clue *what* was done in that airy, empty space one entered if one crashed the waistbarrier. Blank. So from the skies I noticed with a detached interest how this thing called sex was gone about. "Well well," I thought, as his hand, which by now felt like a giant's hand, of a scale commensurate with my fast merging into outer space, "This is what they do." Noting the customs of a foreign country. Look, yams grow here. See, colors are different. No judgment. No personal opinion. Fact of life. In this unexplored country of sexual activity hands go between legs and . . .

He touched a sleeping beauty—my clitoris. Never before touched, unawakened, *it* knew its function and triggered off my responses even though I had been unaware of its existence. As he touched, the gear changed again. I felt upside down. I had started to dive. At first I moved smoothly through the air. Then the diver hit the water and proceeded deeper downward. Then reversed once more.

Now I was being propelled upward, through cloud and sky, and then, as Arne's hand began to move with the confidence of his experience or else sheer marvelous instinct (subsequently in our association we never *spoke* enough for me to find out which), I hit the denser, deeper, medium which parted as I rose up toward it, and drew me into it, closing behind me when it had received me and sucking me further, further . . .

"Oh," I thought, with what there was left of me to think, as Arne first touched me. "So *this* is what sex is like. No wonder everybody . . ." I never finished the sentence in my mind. That denser air engulfed me, and as I was drawn into it, so everything was forgotten.

Even looking back I can't tell whether Arne's instinct was miraculous, or whether I received an imprint of responses from his movements because I was new, so utterly unwritten on, that however he had behaved I would have responded perfectly, having no training or conditioning or habit in this innocent world. Whatever it was, his timing was perfect. There was a moment, before I was so totally drawn to delight, just as the long ride began, when I knew that he *must not stop,* it was a law of nature that he could not abort this launch. But so imperative was it that I should be sent through space toward my being's destination (for that is really how it was to me) that I knew, or trusted, that he *could* not fail. He would not be allowed to stop before the right moment. I didn't know then that there were physiological signs which could be read.

The *affaire* with Arne continued until he left town for the long summer holidays. It was contact, in any social or personal sense, made through a fog of nonperception so thick that I don't think either of us—well not me, certainly—paid much attention to those bits. The physical contact was

sharp, distinct, made in clear air and totally remembered from one time to the next.

But already I was schizophrenic: two people,
at *least*. Having fled young the diminishments of
my native environment, away from the moth-
eaten, daunted adults and their cosily furnished
plugholes, I had run into some trouble. My own
perceptions seemed too simple and unentangled
for the knowing world at which I aimed myself. I
wanted to be a "knower," or rather, in the first instance, because I knew I was young and had a lot
to learn, to associate myself with knowers.

The impulse was right, so I see with hindsight,
but I was already too chickenhearted, too confused by the conflicting propagandas around me,
and chiefly too *greedy* to get going with my life
and do what I had to do (which was to associate with knowers), that I listened for the note of
certainty in people without looking too closely at
what they chose to be certain of. The *taste* of that
emotion was sufficient: gluttonously, I plugged
myself into it wherever I found it, heavy after
each emotional fix, responding to the energiz-
ing flavor of certainty and prepared to be blind
to the personality through which it was chan-
neled.

The result was, I became the darling of the
worst and most boring people in town: valuable
social talismans but little else. Anyone who could
utter a firm opinion about almost anything, anyone so lacking in imagination that his actions were
never hesitant, anyone who laid down the law
with any firmness, who spouted ideas I couldn't
understand, could light a spluttering flame in me

and take payment in the charge of my wide-eyed worship. But it was a small and limited light, because I couldn't really *understand* what they said and therefore could not maintain the glow.

I was the perfect mark for the mystifier.

The clear light of my own perceptions and intuitions was so remarkably *obvious,* I thought (time has told me in fact that sadder, older people value such lost understandings) that what *I* knew could not possibly be the point of this strange game we all seemed to be on earth to play: especially as my knowledge seemed to interest no one at all. Nobody else in fact, ever seemed to notice that lucid world.

And as they were my elders and betters, it was necessary for me to do as they did. The world's training had "took."

Arne didn't fit into the world of social whirling. That world was one of paper and talk. What mattered was what Arne and I *did.*

Arne would take me out. We would go, perhaps to a concert, and I would sit there, dizzy in my mental dark, waiting for the moment when we got back to my room and the light would come on as we touched.

I remember him once saying nervously: "I'm going to get very unpopular with your friends, you know" and wondering why he thought so.

I remember gazing around the concert hall (this was during the intermission) and noticing a cluster of my day-to-day, roll-about, chat-up associates watching me. But *that* world had so little connection with Arne that I had no feeling that I should join the two by word or action. The split was to last for years: clarity and dusk coexisting, and me commuting between the two.

It must have been the same for Arne as for me.

"I could never take you home," he once said. He had probably been considering it. "My parents would throw a fit."

The remark vaguely penetrated. Why did he think he had to? I didn't ask, but he explained, with the first lascivious look I had ever seen on his face:

"They are very anti-Semitic."

Oh.

I'd never come across too much of this. When I met with it I merely thought it such an odd and embarrassing way for someone to think that I would try not to notice it, on their behalf. Rather in the way I still cringe on behalf of name droppers. Well, Arne, I don't want to go to your home; I want you to put your hand between my legs and lie with the length of your body touching mine, and ride with me to the stars. Maybe my lack of experience and expectation was matched in him, and so, mirror to mirror, unknown to unknown, we turned each other on. We made love only in my bed, his penis straight inside and up me, holding me fast, sealing me to him, until I and he were Other, and me on a kind of ladder going upward, upward, with a dozen satisfying landing stages on the way to blot-out.

But I had my pants off and his hand was in me wherever it could be done: in cinemas, in his parked car, on the gritty beach; wherever we were alone.

We were nest animals.

And without connection to any of this, I was working, flirting, smiling, dancing, and worrying with the half-people to whom I was magnetized. They, I felt, constituted my real life: this is the world that mattered to my world: or rather mattered to the relics of my guardians, squatting in my psyche.

They were the unknowns, the nuts that had to be cracked, the withholders of the secret. This was where the lessons would lie.

The world. My oyster.

Arne was only my pearl, whom I already knew.

My heart was not caught and wrung by Arne, because again there were no rules in our game. We had left our respective games and come to each other, and when we met or arranged to meet it was with secure casualness never undermined by failed dates or duplicity. And so, when the time came to go, at the end of term, we said goodbye equally casually.

And when he returned three months later we had both forgotten about each other. We ran into each other only once briefly. "You look older," he said with some surprise.

"Do I?"

His eyes were still that bright blue, and I wouldn't have minded going to bed with him, but my current and his were pulling us different ways, and neither of us minded.

Now I know why we didn't mind. The culture had never taught us—or any of us—to take care of what was of value. The culture had taught us only to value what was rare—and our encounter was so right and easy that we didn't yet know how rare it was. It is right to let go with such ease. If all encounters were equally in clear light we would all let each other go with ease.

Clear light, real life, must be quite a different kind of life from the one we half-people call life.

Years later, I once had phenomenal luck the first day I went out junk hunting. I saw three perfect metal boxes, so beautiful—for what they were they were *that* so properly—that they stood in clear light; a small washed-light aura around them. They were all well within the reach of my pocket. But the lesson still had not been learned: that value is related to intrinsic nature and not only to scarcity—though what is scarce, must, of course, if valuable, be safeguarded with utter carefulness. I was once again greedy. I thought: "If I see three such lovely things the first time I come out, perhaps by waiting I shall find better and cheaper ones. I shouldn't take the first thing I see."

I never did see others as good or as cheap. I *have* seen others since, as beautiful—at great prices, well beyond my means. And I see them in a special way because I know that they are indeed infrequent.

And that, too, is the way I see my fledgling relationship with Arne.

## Chapter 4

There were no more beads in my necklace for a long time. The dark took over. For the first time, I had localized a source for my light-beads ("sex" is where you find them, they are made by a penis plugging into your endless socket) and now I went hunting for them. I grabbed for them in motor cars, impatiently waded through conversations at dinner parties waiting for the moment when I would have charmed the man enough to offer me a lift home, hunted on beds waiting for the light to be switched on, and failing, failing.

For I had begun to do the sterilizing unforgivable. I was hunting for my beads now in the dark of the world; among the strange other-creatures I longed to approximate to; the persons who moved confidently among the implausible peculiarities of day-to-day life; the ones who seemed to know: whose aspirations went without hesitation toward money, girl-getting, or (much more seductive to the seeker and yearner inside of me) the fashionable abstract, the incomprehensible philosophies of the time.

I was a pushover for anyone who spouted, say, existentialism in such a way that it made no sense at all. If it made a little bit of sense, he was instantly less attractive. Marxists whose eyes were so clotted with frenzy that they could neither see nor talk straight, who laid down the law for all other people with such total closure that there was nothing left to squeak or wriggle or breathe; these were my magically attractive beings; my monsters made beautiful. Made, indeed irresistible. Other beauties may have loved beasts not suspecting they were princes. But I saw princes where all around were beasts. I can now no longer remember the dizzying number of the beast-brigade: all the possessors of arrogance, selfishness, ungovernable temper, lofty nonsense . . . I embraced them all, and tried to call out from them the pearl that would hold the longed-for light.

It never worked. I was trying to join the impalpable, the unalterable, to the mocked-up litter, the flotsam and debris which had fallen on the beaches of the world. Like a greedy savage who had once or twice seen fire made, I tried to work the magic myself: hopefully, clumsily, sticking the electric lead into the mud, just in *case* it worked. I tried and tried and pushed and pushed. And joined the vast ranks of women who could not have orgasms. I went part of the way often; sometimes I went no distance at all. But I couldn't find the fire again. Stubbornly I pulled and heaved, looking for the core of idealism in my be-

guiling monsters that I could breathe into fire;
hoping to bring them to that clear state of mind
thereby which would meet and spark my own.

A friend who had observed all this, told me
years later: "All those men! They had no *idea* what
you wanted."

They would dredge deep in themselves for some
remnant, some broken barnacled relic to offer me,
hoping that this was the gift I was after. And the
more broken toys they offered, the more I would
pull; and when I had got to their deeps and still
not found there what I wanted, then I would
walk away. Leaving them baffled.

And then there were the pretenders who could
not offer this, who humored or bullied or patron-
ized me—turning me, because of my habit and
training, into an eager and hopeful puppydog,
hoping they would tell me their secret if I
wagged my tail hard enough.

*There were, as well, the Terrifying others,*
*whom I took care not to get too close to, because*
*instinct told me that indeed they could light me;*
*that they might drive me into another place and*
*not be capable of bringing me back: who would*
*send me mad, in fact, and leave me to find my*
*own way home.*

*These were the ones who were going on their*
*own searches, with whom I might indeed have*
*made my way, had the structure of my personality*
*been solid enough. But I knew that with these*
*my own falseness and equivocations and ambi-*
*tions and settlements would have been burnt out*
*in the first explosion into light; in that endless,*

*driving orgasm. And who would come back? Having met the radiant bead-seeker, would they want the empty no-one?*

*I wooed them with my ego, but I knew that, if indeed I did return, from the rocket-trip, my ego would be burned out. No thank you. Leave me my crutch.*

Ambition and greed kept me from these. I *had* to dive through the puzzle world of the monsters and understand what was going on; what the mystery was.

So I thought.

These had the secret.

So I thought.

After all, I already knew that other secret.

And so I plunged onward, avoiding more and more those who could have helped and shown and been companions; turned on still by status, and success, and a spurious knowingness. I became prodigiously successful in my own right, fueled by my desire to meet the most successful people I could conceive of, and drawn further away from those with whom I might have added another bead to my necklace, or even created a real channel of communication or light. Before I had been schizophrenic, inhabiting two worlds. I both knew and didn't know. The drinking horse forgot; but the horse at the water's edge, refusing to drink, was unviolated. They coexisted.

But now the one who knew, the place where the brightness was known, the sanctuary where I hid my beads of light, was visited so seldom that layers of dark and dust, and forgotten, discarded thoughts, covered it over. I was always aware of its existence, but paid it less and less attention. Instead, I was the rich and clever and successful and evasive child of the world, the darling of my social scene, selecting the beds I would sleep in and the men I would join with in inverse proportion to the power they had to light my fire.

During the period before I married, which I did when I was twenty, I had all the experience one needs as raw material for drawing sufficient conclusions about human behavior in the strange land called sex—had I inspected it, or even remembered it.

For instance, before Arne, I already had been approached by an exhibitionist. He was standing blocking my path, but his fly zip got stuck as I got closer and closer, and there he was wrestling with yet one more example of bad workmanship, desperately trying to get it open and out and up before I walked by giggling.

Approached, also, by one child molester (I was about eleven) whom I simply thought was trying to kidnap me just as "they" did in adventure stories. So I led him on, conscious of having an adventure from which I could escape when I wanted, to the very door of his apartment. And then ran as fast as my heels could carry me down the stairs and along the street and home. Recorded it in my diary: "Almost kidnapped today. Baked beans for supper. Dad in rotten temper."

And approached, finally, by one nymphet-chaser, while I was on a seaside holiday with my stepdad. He was a married man whom I thought terrific because he had the good looks and style of those upper-class men in films (his voice thrilled me . . . all those clean, clipped British vowels) and he was suave and indifferent to almost anything except drinking, manlylike, in the bar, and looking sporty on the beach.

Bunny, the ruddy-faced car salesman. He waited patiently on my bed one night, huge erection in hand, until I came upstairs. (Query: how did he *get* there? Probably had it away with the chambermaid in passing.) However it happened that he'd gained access, that was the only access he managed. He sat heavily, huge cock rosy and waving (it was my first sight of a cock, and I simply didn't register it as anything except another of life's surprises), reaching for my hand to bring it to his pole, murmuring drunken, passionate lust-gasps. I felt rather as I did about anti-Semites and name-droppers. Didn't he realize what a sad situation he'd placed himself in? Goodness, how embarrassing for him. With confident determination and all the good manners at my command, I eased him out and lay in bed reflecting on the event, flattered that he had thought me nice enough to "fall in love" with. Of course, it wasn't quite as smooth as all that:

"You must go, Bunny. I want to go to bed."

"Yes, what a good idea."

"No, no. I can't while you're here.

"My dad will hear us, you must GO." (Stepfather and aunt scared me far more than the rampant sex-bone, waving like a radar beacon in the torrid sea breeze. My parents were known di-

sasters; the needs of this romantic elderly gent—
hindsight tells me he must have been about thirty-
three—were unknown, and surely not to be dealt
with by someone as green as I: he had made a
mistake, and needed one of those gorgeous sophisticated women out of the films.)

"I want you so much."

"Don't be silly."

"*Now* who's making a noise. Come here, you
bitch."

"No! I'll see you on the beach tomorrow."

"Let me see you now. I want to see those
breasts."

NO! (They were huge and good, but they
weren't the Hollywood duco-glossed, biscuit-
colored, lacquered affairs which I imagined would
be consonant with his stylish needs.)

"I've seen them anyway. When you were
changing to swim. They're beautiful . . . let me
hold them."

(???? Was he a peeper as well? How had he
got to see them? Poor man, how terrible. Let's get
him out fast.)

"Just put your hand there for a moment."

NO. NO. NO.

And I shoved him out, fly open, mouth open,
drunk, amazed, and bounded into bed, awed.

*I rated!*

When I saw him next morning, I still thought
he was terrific and romantic and suave and . . .
how else could the events of the night be con-
strued . . . even more remarkable, in love with
ME. I danced up to him with delight, as I had

right through the holiday, because I liked the cosmopolitan (so I thought) and wicked flavor of his company.

Bunny, to his credit, didn't act as though the evening's fumbling made any difference either.

We went home next day, and for a few weeks he remained in my mind as one of my most exciting conquests.

# Chapter 5

I became a photographer, working in the photographic department of the local newspaper; my first job, more or less as a glorified tea-maker and messenger girl, and. . . .

Into the department one day stalked the Arch-Knower of all time. A Real-Life, True-Life, Much-Traveled, Deeply-Seamed-of-Face Chief Foreign Correspondent of a BIG MASS BRITISH DAILY. Wow! In terms of the Knowers in the mysterious muddle-world, here was the prize, the plum, the bull's-eye, the super-plus-fire-lighter.

He Deigned to Notice me. And how could he not? I was flickering like a pinball machine when the score mounts high.

He must have seen a pretty young girl, avid for whatever he might be in mind to suggest, and so he suggested dinner. We went to a romantic, leafy, whitewashed bungalow-hotel on the mountainside, with the sea not in sight but within both hearing and minds-memory. There were zinnias in the vase on the table, and the iced yellow wine made freezing water-drops on my crystal glass. He talked, and I stared steady and attentive, sliding oozy, creamy, smooth substances unnoticed over my ready-tasting tongue.

And oh how he talked!

I let him go on and on, waiting for the moment when the secrets of the vast world outside the Australian bush would be revealed; the movements of peoples, the minds of premiers, fragments from the lives of the great and the wise and the famous.

The orchestra looked at us; saw, no doubt, my rapt and flushed face. The violinist sauntered over and played some *zigeuner* phrases for us two alone.

Ralph paused while the violinist attended us. And then continued.

But he was, oddly, withholding the secrets of his wide experience—except in one smutty quarter. He seemed to need, to my surprise, to talk compulsively about the dirty things he had done with his wife, with girls the world over, with prostitutes, with almost anyone who had a taste for being chained, whipped, beaten, blindfolded, and tortured on their way to sexual ecstasy. I dragged it all out of him with the same serious absorption. If I could just go on pulling and pulling until he's *said* it all (and as, apparently, it fascinated him, I had a social duty to appear as if it was fascinating me, for he *was* paying for the meal) then perhaps we could proceed to the really *hot* stuff. About the world. About real life.

About the interesting countries he'd visited and the interesting events he'd witnessed.

Nothing, not a single thing, that he said excited me. No expectation, again. Ignorant that this was "supposed" to happen, it did not.

In retrospect, I can hardly believe it, searching my memory for traces that I might be fooling myself. No. In the years since, I have learned that certain verbal descriptions of human behavior, wrecked, wretched, blotty, and sore, are intended to produce a charge and they can, sometimes, produce a charge in me.

But not then. And not the reality. Not handsome, bloodhound Ralph, rat-tatting away. He should have taken another look at his quarry: had he talked about meeting Albert Schweitzer I would have spread my legs before dessert.

But like a rhino in full charge, he couldn't change course. He must have been waiting for some reaction from me; some signal that I was either disgusted or turned on. Nothing came. As the wine was poured and repoured, my face became warmer and probably pinker, my eyes possibly glazed over a bit, and my speech no doubt became more deliberate and careful. I do remember that before my eyes came a procession of ungainly animals, Ralph's face changing from warthog to hippo to kangaroo to frog as his tongue wagged and the words waved and I stared on, amazed and unwavering.

Undone by my apparent inability ever to hear enough, Ralph extended himself further than he meant to. As before, when my boyfriends had dragged their very sea depths for the phrase that would turn the trick, so Ralph began to puzzle and flail, reaching for enormity after enormity to discover which would contain the miracle loosener.

How about the time when he chained his wife, spreadeagled, to the bed, peed all over her, and then had the dog lick her off?

No?

No flicker from the demure, degenerate, avid child?

Or the time they went on holiday, her hands chained invisibly behind a cape, and he forcing her to her pleasure over the knob of the gear lever? No?

Obviously, action was needed. He paid the bill and drove me, mazily, back to my bedsit.

Where I, too, was waiting for action, of quite another kind. Now, perhaps, thought I, we would *get* somewhere.

Or perhaps, if he wouldn't tell me about the world, he would love me as Arne had. He seemed to have such wide experience of peculiar things that a simple little matter such as straightforward lovemaking would surely find him consummate in its art.

But I remember us reaching the garden path, and him being sick on it. Then a flare of memory finds us in my room, with Ralph, head in hands, begging hoarsely for black tea. And then it shows him standing, holding my two hands in his, saying he is sorry, saying he must get back to his hotel.

Puzzled, intrigued, and once again unmolested, I went to bed and thought about the strange people who lived in the remarkable world across the seas.

Thus, before I was twenty, I had experienced a cavalcade of grotesques, and one true event.

The true event was burned clear in my consciousness; the grotesques had pranced and sprawled and waggled their cocks and stuck out their bums, and faded.

They were many. After all, a year is a long time—one only needs a few hours of grotesquery every several days to produce two or three score.

Many was the time, you could call it a pastime, when I would draw someone out in conversation beyond his endurance, so that he would collapse, pie-eyed and plastered, before what he had planned took place. I was unaware of my own part in all this, and began to think that a vast army of suave older men were incapable of all the things they bragged of during daylight hours; those things privy to overhearing, working as I did in the male precinct of a newspaper office, and the photographers'—notoriously bawdy—section at that.

But there was, as well, another part of the picture. Down in dockland, where I mixed with people who had no pretense, I found that my noncombatant status in the sex game was understood, noted, and regarded as a characteristic of *me*.

I got on well with these people. They did not see a pressbutton set of stimuli and behave according to their preordained estimate of "dollies." When they needed sex-buttons pressed, as opposed to the eat-buttons of a cup of coffee or the social-buttons of a chat, or the recreational-buttons of a walk by the boats, past the oily hawsers; then they went to professionals whose job it was, or to old or new friends quite openly willing so to contract.

Had such a concept been invented in those days, I would have been called delinquent. But in fact there was nothing any more squalid down in the docks than existed uptown. The complacent Ralph, the smug-fat Dick (who invited me to a party and received me on his own, naked and drunk), even the sly-grabbing Bunny were no better (or worse) than my malfunctioning friends, the outcasts. Except that the outcasts could give straight companionship in a way the suave brigade found not so much difficult as incomprehensible, belonging to some other, unprofitable, order of behavior.

# Chapter 6

If it had not been for an unfortunate accident, an act of murder, so I thought of it, I might have continued as I began until it dawned on me that nothing was what it seemed; that I might as well make up my own mind about all aspects of the puzzle, personal, sexual, relational, and so on, just as I was doing more than adequately professionally, where everything seemed cut and dried.

There, at least, challenges were set up, you approached them in a more or less straightforward way, and depending on your energy and capacity for hard work, you made it.

In the end, I might have decided the same about this other field of hazard, but for the mess that Jeffrey and I made between us.

It was about eighteen months after Arne. Jeffrey was much older; in his late twenties I think, straw-colored and freckled; catlike, lazy speeched, an ex-soldier from the wars. He was the first son-

of-friends-of-my-family whom I respected as a
knower and traveler in the great Out-There. The
world was moving closer! There were whispered
stories and disapproving nods and grunts over the
bridge table, sometimes, when his name came up
and I was passing tea for my mother's friends.
What was more, he had that igniting quality of
certainty. Only now do I know that it was lassi-
tude, *laissez-faire*, and laziness; the line of least
resistance.

We met at a dance—square, middle rich, dull—
with soft, deeply cushioned chairs in the sitting
room and a buffet table that looked as if some gas-
tronomic-geared computer had been programmed
to produce high-grade, machine-sculpted versions
of the photographs in Hungarian cookbooks. Older women wore satin, smooth, and stiff over their
rumps; pearls and "costume jewelry" decorated
tired, too-tanned female skin. Not my scene.
Among such people I became computer programmed too: a fair facsimile of the unmarried
daughter edging onto the shelf. Hell, I was nine-
teen. But in those days and circles I was getting
on: watched speculatively for signs of pairing off
with a suitable up-and-coming son.

I was there because my parents had been getting angry at the numbers of "suitable" dates I
had been refusing, and it was reaching the levels
of intolerable. So I went with this "suitable" David (they would have been shocked if they knew
how this "suitable" dandy behaved toward me),
of whom they mightily approved. The first time
he took me out he bought me an overornate box
of chocolates and put his arm around me in the

cinema. The next time he tried some heavy petting in the car. I resisted. The third time he tried treating me like a chum. I resented it. The last time, which would be later that night (perhaps stimulated by my response to Jeffrey), he asked me to go to bed with him. "Of course not," I hissed. "Well, what *do* you want, then," he said helplessly. He'd been through the only alternatives he was aware of. "Some ordinary human interchange, for a start, you fool." "*Oh*, you're complicated."

My commuting between the dockside and the dances was so natural that I doubt if anyone realized how diverse my social arrangements were —though David might have sensed that something curious was going on and therefore asked me to go to bed with him. For this was simply NOT DONE in the circles to which we both belonged—not with another founder member. Axiomatically I was a virgin, and to be well treated. Which meant: not taken to bed. Curiously though, if I put out in a motor car, that was somehow within the rules.

So there we were at this dance. We were sitting with David's older sister and her rich, boring husband when Jeffrey hailed David, and joined us. David and I had been gazing bleakly at each other. I was feeling cross, superior, and impatient, and racking my brains for something pleasantly neutral to say. Jeffrey gazed appraisingly at me —and until he left my life again that, I'm afraid, was the last time I had the pleasure of feeling cross, superior, impatient—or even neutral.

It turned out that Jeffrey was back in the country from fighting in a war. He'd lived several months in a seaside town some four hundred miles away, and packed it in for some reason, and was now here, staying with his family for a while. His context, it appeared, was cultivated and literary: a blood-milieu utterly alien from my own displaced, slum-jumped, culture-shocked, memory-frozen, sea-torn kin.

He was a sophisticate.

If we were all a mad computer's creatures that night, eating processed-people-food and dancing processed-people-jumps, and talking processed-people-talk, then Jeffrey was my personal processed nemesis—spat out of the machine and landed at my feet, packaged for accident. This is not to give him personally an importance, or scale, which he does not deserve.

After all, an individual can break his neck by tripping over a stone.

And it was *my* neck.

Sophisticated Jeffrey asked me to dance. At first a mild, sexual current trickled between us, nothing knockout, but bumped-up and exacerbated by Jeffrey's certainty, his blondness (a color to which, since Arne, I had been, if not imprinted, certainly frequently drawn) and his apparent amused, butter-voiced contempt for everything around him.

His cold eye on the scene made me aware that in his ranging travels he must have seen better appointments, heard finer music, and graced more glittering dance parties than this one. Somewhere, or so I misread from his manner, he had consorted with the "knowers"—those people who played the mysterious game of life deftly, with panache, because they actually knew why we were all heaving about in this peculiar roundelay, and therefore had high style.

Only later did I tumble to the fact that the style existed because in fact they had given up the search to know, and had all their energies available for stylishness as an interesting end in itself; devoted their talents to acquiring it; their aspiration into perfecting it. Jeffrey had Style, in this way. Somewhere, in his stylish Ur-world, long lines of glistening women, as amused and cool, as sophisticated as he, straight from the admags, shellacked and rigid with poise, writhed and tossed and toiled and teased in his memory.

All I needed to do was to visualize these images with some clarity to have had them collapse: wrongly joined dolls, unviable chimeras. But I saw them through my mental fog: alluring sirens; beguiling, impossible others; the She's beyond the seas.

A little light on the matter and the whole image would have twisted, curled, and vaporized. Up in smoke. But the forests of my mind held such unbelievable creatures in those days.

And there he was. Jeffrey. Him Tarzan. Me Rabbit. And Rabbit was mesmerized as the representative from the big world, straw-colored, buttercolored, honey-colored Jeffrey, cocked his finger, jerked his head, and raised his eyebrows. Rabbit rose, will-less, to dance.

The fact that tawny Tarzan couldn't meet Rabbit's eyes seemed reasonable: I assumed merely that he was consorting with the seductive Others of his memory, and it was the duty of mundane Rabbit-girl to woo his mind away from them. The

fact that his mouth was wired for sneer struck me
only as the essence of sophisticated world-weari-
ness.

And so we danced, I confused by the suffusion
of excitement which the unknown always released
in me, priming me each time with new hope, for
the clear light of real happening—confused it, because I desired to. With hindsight there is a no-
table difference between these varieties of excitement; at the time they were indistinguishable.

Underneath, as always underneath, lay the sub-
marine sorting-house, the clearing-hall in which
what was real and what was false could easily be
reckoned. But I would have had to dive to reach
it, and by now I was habituated to swimming in
the shallows.

Within days I was Jeffrey's plaything and pup-
py-rabbit. From wearing my girlhood with ease
and naturalness I became a nervous supplicant. I
was anxious not to be a bore (something which
had never occurred to me before), and in being
so became one. Alert to fascinate him, my voice
would shrill to a high false note as I strained for
coy tricks and flirtatious ways which up till then
had been second nature. Like some pasha of de-
generated legend, he sat there waiting to be
amused, to be served aright; noting how often I
failed, and taking it out on me by refusing to make
love to me that night, tantalizing me with speculation about whether he would or would not.

Actually, the love-making was a bore, if I'd had
wits enough remaining to notice. But there was
one novel aspect about it: Jeffrey was the first to

name names. Given that it was neither right nor proper—and fortunately I had the memory of Arne as a touchstone, and even without the memory would have had a less material touchstone, for women carry the knowledge of the perfect, and how it should be, within them, even if they never reach it once in the whole of their lives—given, then, that it was neither right nor proper, Jeffrey was the first in my experience to take sex out of the wrapping-ribbons of half-truth and endearment and imitation of what should be, and lay it on the line.

He knew what he wanted. "Shift your cunt." "Grab my cock." "Faster." "Now put it in." He offered the lineaments of lust, but really, so tamely. He had a Rabbit in his bed, after all. Rabbit was a handy receptacle for his lust. "If I've got to come somewhere, it might as well be in her"— so he projected his attitude toward the whole business. She seems to want to stick around, so she can jolly well make herself useful.

"That's right: up a bit."

Shift.

"Higher."

Shift shift.

"OK now. Stop a moment." Jeffrey roists about inside me, finding comfortable lodgings and settling in for a long haul.

"Hips up."

Shift shift.

Pause.

All these *orders*. My mind wanders, wondering what he's feeling. I feel only locally, specifically, and physically where his flesh which has waved in the world's air touches my flesh which has never been open to it, except through the touch of the masculine stranger. Where he did not touch, I did not feel: no waves, no travelings.

"Shove that pillow under you."

Shift.

"OK—get your legs up. Over my neck."

Shift shift.

"Further."

Shift.

Gear engaged. "Right. Here I go."

All I could respond with was "Bon Voyage." I was not sailing that day.

*So many people inhabit one. Jeffrey had a rabbit in his bed because rabbit was all he could summon out of me. But always available to me up till that point had been a variety of old Knowledges. I could, as it were, tune into them. Tune into "flirt," and tap the knowledge of generations of funny, flirtatious, bright, and tantalizing women. Tune into "queen," and become a majesty, attracting devotion, honor, and service. I could tune and beam higher, too, into states without names for setting down here, and let that particular knowledge, too, form itself sexually and run through the impalpable pool of such knowledge and from the impalpable Representatives of such knowledge straight into my body, and through me, into the hanging globe of sexual concourse. But this capacity, underexercised and hardly awarely known as yet; my birthright and confident heritage; unexplored but familiar and easy of access; these states had to be called out.*

But Jeffrey called for nothing except a stable-mate, a variety of animals. A rabbit to frighten. At best, a pig to poke. He called for little and projected a lot. And so it was, tame and meanly, poke, poke, push, pull, that's better, turn over, hips up, bum out, poke and roil, there we go my girl.

Though *where* we went I have no idea. In spite of my waving him off, so to speak, at the quayside, it couldn't have been far—for his journey, after all, did depend to a great extent on me. From my own sense of those occasions, I would say he went into a centrifugal spin around my access; as if my cunt-tip were the navel of a little world, a securely anchored island, and he was all penis, a long, skinny, elastic penis wielding a tiny manikin, whirling the little homunculus in orbit round and round the nubbin island. Until the impetus ran out. In failing to get me going, he failed to fuel a journey for himself. He could only, so I think, have had a supercolossal fairground spin, going no distance, however his senses whirled. If he thought it was Luna Park, then that was his problem. He would whizz and jizz about, have his spasm and stop, while I lay sweating but stony, waiting for him to rest, and then seeking to continue, to *begin*.

But Jeffrey would spend no more. One merry-go-round fare was enough. He would turn his back and sleep it off.

Our affair lasted a couple of months. Boring couplings in my bedsit or his mother's house when they went away for the weekend. The routine dinner in a restaurant before the fuck (but only if Jeffrey felt like a good meal first, I suspect) with

Jeffrey often moody and the two of us off in our silences.

Once the French letter broke. I panicked. Jeffrey became animated for a surprisingly long spell, and made a succession of jokes about it which I simultaneously considered to be poor taste and marveled at as a pennant for High Style.

What did Jeffrey see in me? A stopgap, so to speak? An articulate declivity, prepared to receive his prick and house his wastes? As I invented him at first, so surely must he have invented me. As he failed to call out what was interesting or considerable in me so I, surely, equally failed in him.

I think he would have been unwilling to turn down something (such devotion!) so freely offered, and I think he must have mocked-up a girl who was something of a hardship case, something of a pain in the ass, and something pleasant—if only she was less jumpy; would come conveniently when called, both in bed and out; and would not make irritating demands, like bed when he wanted silence, or food when he wanted fuck, or reassurance when he was feeling murderous. But most of all I think he was unable to steer me into the balance he would have liked—somewhere between a convenient fuck and a girl on tap, but nowhere near his ordinary life and his friends and social movements.

That was where I would like to have gone with him: among his sophisticated companions. And that, of course, is where embarrassing rabbit-girl was steered away from. I treated him as a thing just ever as much as he did me.

But younger and less scarred by the world as I was, I had a great deal more to lose. He wanted to keep me, a doll in a cupboard, for the moments when he felt like opening the door, taking me out, and playing with me. I wanted to have orgasms with him, but having failed in that, then at least to have him handy, a social solvent, oozing me toward the people I wanted to know; my facsimile of a boyfriend among the people who thought I was strangely retarded in my social-emotional life.

Basically, of course, he didn't want much: not a tenth as much of the emotional and other gift I was trying to make him. But what he wanted had to *look* approximately the way he wanted it—and by giving him too much I gave him nothing at all, and voided all my own growth-potential for years by staying on with him.

Jeffrey—the point of Jeffrey, not the person of Jeffrey—was the start of real waste. Many cultures frame, in one way or another, the fact that there are both moments and places where, as the aborigines put it, there exists what they called a Knot of Time, where past, present, and future meet, and are joined together. Each individual is a culture, living in his own personal air. Jeffrey penetrated my personal air; he coincided with a personal Knot of Time.

From that rupture of my personal air, from that Knot of Time, leaked away my growth-potential. Specifically, the broken French Letter produced a fetus.

I dialed Jeffrey and told him.

Pause. And what I interpreted as a suffering sigh.

"Well, what are you going to do then?" he asked.

"I don't know yet, Jeffrey. What do you think?"

Pause.

"It's up to you. Let me know when you've decided. It's your problem."

Silence.

Click.

I had hoped for support, or even some slight contact.

Nothing.

Things got complicated at that point. Three days later my appendix burst. I came through the operation with the baby, or what would have been a baby, intact. As I lay on the table, the doctor to whom I had confided my problem, murmured to the surgeon: "Just shove a little there," a request of real bravery, for he was dead respectable. "While you've got her open, just give that a bit of a push."

The surgeon, ethical, refused.

Abortions in those days had routine attendant terrors. The money which had to be found. The mandatory espionage—though those with whom I became involved had an unnecessary flair for the dramatic.

They required me to make a long journey to an unknown, drab, and draughty part of the city, wait on a corner by a church for my Contact, change cars twice, and be brought (they wanted to blindfold me but I said I'd shut my eyes) in the dark to my Deliverer, the Midwife. And Midwife stood, brandishing (garnished by horrified imagination) a carving knife, baring her teeth in Smile, and laid one down, facing the yellowing wall, on a lace-covered bed protected with a transparent plastic sheet, just below a crucifix and a picture of the Virgin Mary on the wall. Outside, slum noises, dogs barking, and the shouts of children at play. Inside me, stabs of pain, as she poked and fiddled up my channel and into my womb's opening with what felt like a length of looped wire, and gave a few sharp tugs. I was still weak from the operation; the stitches had been taken out that morning.

Brawny, muscular, butchering Midwife, she of the inordinate biceps, to her I felt it necessary to owe and show gratitude, over and above the exorbitant cash. Another example of tangled wires. Business is business, after all. The Jewish community, which for some reason had failed to teach me so much else, had failed, even, to pass on to me that valuable precept of our heritage.

"This your first time?" Midwife-Giant asked, practical, conversational, as she propelled me firmly to the front door.

"Yes, it is."

"Don't worry. You'll be all right."

"Thank you then. Goodbye."

"Goodbye till next time, dear. You'll be back. The girls come up in their lunch hours."

And it was that—not the pain, nor the fatigue, nor the self-pity, nor the misery, but that acceptance of an endless unbreakable circle—that was what made me, on the instant, vomit, and then keel into a faint.

Jeffrey had left town, so I discovered, on what must have been the day after I phoned him.

I hadn't expected that. Somewhere, I was thinking that because we were of the same social tribe —his parents, though so much more elevated, still knew my parents, and he even was related to my *doctor*, for God's sake—somehow he would see the thing through with me, even marry me if he had to. In the crunch, our tribe was decent, wasn't it? I was still sufficiently brainwashed to resort, in emergencies, to my tribal axioms and not look at the individuals concerned. My lot were Reliable, unlike my dockland or photographer friends from whom I expected no loyalty. The fact that often, delighted and embarrassed, I received it from *them*, had not registered.

Within the week I heard that Jeffrey was a thousand miles away. Scooted like the rabbit I thought I was.

Within the month a friend remarked casually, while a number of us were sitting idly in a cafe: "Jeffrey? Oh, he's in . . . Got a girl into trouble and had to leave. Seems to make a habit of it. That's why he came here in the first place: knocked a girl up in the last town too. Poor guy."

Silently, I thanked my furious compulsion to keep my sex life secret, and Jeffrey's determination not to have us seen out too much together. I would have hated the loss of face involved with my casual friends had they known I was the girl.

But "poor guy"? Why feel sorry for *him*? What about me, curled up hour after screaming hour like the fetus I had tried to abort, rolling myself into a tight ball to keep the child inside me after the Lady-Butcher had taken it away; me, weeping and sweating at the thought of it loosed from

my womb? Poor *guy*? Later, I understood that this
was fair comment, even if made spuriously. In the
long term, poor guy. When the tales are all told,
when all the facts are in, there is a true and neutral justice and balancing at work.

Poor guy.

# Chapter 7

And shortly afterward, Poor Rabbit made straight
for her funk-hole. The reasoning, which I surfaced
only years later, but which was blind and unde-
viating nonetheless for its unconsciousness, went
like this: "The whole game of this life is beyond
me. Meaningless and confused beyond hope of
disentangling. In all my tries at finding out what
we're up to, only one unarguable fact has emerged.
My way has led to murder. 'Their way' (Them
—the Others—in my case family and social tribe,
dull and defeated, every last one of them) . . . their
way at least has a built-in safety factor. Go in and
hide safely. Whoops, Alice, down you go . . .
straight down the rabbit-hole."

Like the alarm bells were all ringing, man. So I
slid down the greasy pole, sat on my personal fire-
engine, and rode posthaste headfirst straight into
the blaze—for after all, the frying pan had been
too much for me.

But I was no slouch when it came to foresight. If I was picking an incinerator, it might as well have all the habiliments and furbishments, as the Ambassador said to the Queen, of A-Class supertype luxury. Not too imposing, for I would incur jealousy, which would be uncomfortable. Not too modest, which might be equally uncomfortable through deprivation. Don't stick your neck out, dear. You've done with all that. Pick carefully— go for fair but not flamboyant comfort.

All that added up to Ben. A bachelor twenty years older than I. A really nice guy. Puzzle that he hadn't married, but there you are. He had a load of cash, but didn't fling it around. Everyone liked him. Well respected. Family and family friends, into whose feathers I nestled after the abortion, all congratulated me. Family Doctor (not he of the abortion, but he of the childhood measles and mumps) looked approving and voiced the collective sentiment: "Well, well," he said in tones of absent-minded relief, gazing at me like a symptom spontaneously remitting in front of his eyes, "All fixed up at last." My granny said:

"So you've come round."

Dead accurate. Back to square one.

Once again, I let me do my own duping. Not having allowed myself to think that I was doing a bunk, retreating into *permanent incarceration* just to lick a few wounds, I had to talk myself into the idea that I loved him.

And by all formula tests I certainly did. He was a textbook Grade-A perfect case for loving. By women's mag standards, by film and family standards, he was Lovable—and these, now, were to

be my standards, deliberately, teeth-grittingly, my
. . . damn . . . standards. I loved him for the safety
of his money, the probity of his personality, the
moderation of his views, the temperateness of his
nature. He was equable, and unwilling to interfere
with others. I loved him for other qualities, too,
qualities which even today I love, as qualities,
wherever I find them, almost without reference
to the day-to-day personality—qualities of restraint,
patience, detachment, and the capacity to let people be; and in letting them, help them be more.

(Qualities I was later to find operated in him
in connection with everyone except his wife.)

But chiefly, let it be said, I loved him because
he did not seem to want to make love to me.
Numbed with shock after Jeffrey, battered by the
endless bouts at which, too often, I had been psy-
chically stunned, I somehow assumed that the wise
and patient Ben, my brand-new husband-to-be,
saw deeply into me, and understood that I was
too raw and wounded for sexual breaching.

The brilliant heroes of romantic novels and those
tear-jerking films understood this. And Ben was
brilliant, everyone said. So the only things that
restrained such heroes, and Ben's mad flaring
passion (this being inherent because we were in
Love), could have been this grand and deep understanding and compassion, couldn't it?

Well no, actually.

But no signals were capable of ripping the self-
deception. Now that my personal air had leaked
away, I had a thoroughgoing case of the psychological bends. Too much nitrogen in my head
spaces, rendering all plain stimuli hallucinatory.

A close friend of Ben's, a randy Chinese scientist whom the paper assigned me to photograph, made a violent pass and nearly raped me. There had been no encouragement from numbskull numbcunt—except the overexercise of charm, which was a profligate professional habit. I'm lovely, I'm engaged, I'm inviolate was my thinking, as I smiled and wheedled and flattered to get my pictures.

The square-cut solitaire diamond, hand-set with such care and bought at such expense, nullifies my sexual charge-up, surely, just as pregnancy does.

I am now A-Nother's. Does he really mean to . . . ?

Just ignore him.

He can't mean to. . . . He knows Ben.

He wouldn't.

Oh. Oh, he would.

Wow, he really would.

It wasn't until my blouse was half ripped off that I surfaced into some kind of survival sense, let loose some sharp, guilt-provoking (I hoped) homilies, and ran.

And poured it all out on Ben, waiting to be buttressed by the Right Romantic Response: Indignation. I'll-Knock-His-Block-Off. Oh-You-Poor-Innocent-Chee . . . I'ld.

Come on, Ben. Say away. Don't look so glum.

Silence.

Unsaid: "Oh, hell. Did you have to. Why do you want to test me? He's my friend."

Said: "Well, what do you want me to do?"

Me: "What do you want to do? I felt awful, you know. It was dreadful."

Ben: "I suppose I should feel jealous or something, but I don't."

New bit of info: Ben doesn't feel jealous.

Old bit of info: Ben doesn't try to make love. Just fatherly kisses and the protective arm around my shoulders.

Put them together now. Adds up to . . . ?

Oh, don't think down there. That'll take you where you dare not go, out out again where the animals savage you, and the savages are senseless.

Think . . . think . . . no tigers here. Think . . . repeat the litany . . . bridal gown, orange blossom, teacups and tablecloths, and your HONEY-MOON . . .

( . . . where it will *All Come Right.*)

See what I mean about being a not-person when one operates in the mental dark?

Lights all off now.

One last taillight, a vanishing gleam in the distance, never quite gone, but requiring eyes trained steady and determined to catch the faint flare.

And the fog coming down solid.

After marriage, some horrid warnings from my dream world, nightmares that rend my throat and envelop me in daytime horrors, so menacing is their remembered flavor.

But the dream itself not remembered, and the flavor not understood.

Goodbye, my light.

Goodbye.

# Chapter 8

Now fog blanketed all.

Here was the beginning of the wilderness.

Marriage a desert waste; nothing really lost for nothing ever gained—but time spent, leaked away.

And so, when my penance was done, I packed my bags, left a note on Ben's pillow, and went to England.

England, land of the Free, turned out to be a vast, soggy wash of pallid zombie-creatures rattling their sexual chains. Where I came from, in the Great Outdoors, we may not have been sensible, our wits might have been addled, we were yokels—but at least our *glands,* so to speak, functioned in a straight-forward manner.

Here, all was twisted and awry. The first time I ever switched on TV I heard a young man with VD complaining that he'd been tricked into bed with a girl. He was asked how much he knew about sex, before that, "Well, I knew it wasn't to stir your tea wiv," he uttered.

Bedded down neatly in the dormitory suburbs, perhaps there were tidy, friendly fuckings going on, and perhaps too, ripe and bursting in the springtime dells or moody in the thunders of Devon and Yorkshire, great tidal passions burgeoned and flashed untamed; but I doubt it. Cosmopolitan sexy London was a mental region, a flux which dragged over the country as far as the Scottish highlands; a low-lying, ragged, oozy cloud of malfunctioning sexual impulses; a muggy swill of twisted wants; a dank, dirty-yellow, glutty fog inside which stumbled and blundered the sexual somnambulists, playing catch-as-catch-can with whomever they bumped in the rancid dark.

Into this wilderness, into the thick of the fog, I now drifted.

*We were a parade of creatures by Kraft-Ebbing, out of Bosch. When the occasional scrag of light lifted the smudgy dark, those of us who were still capable stood thickly to attention, momentarily sobered, peering with fright, then wincing away from the sight, shape, scale of the deformities revealed. Perhaps it was good fortune that the worst specimens were totally blind, and so never would catch sight of the misshapen pallor, the wronggone wretchedness, of their companions and themselves.*

*We were a nasty lot: a pathological, posturing sideshow; freaks one and all. There were creatures who called themselves men, but who lisped and were baby-shy, wearing diapers and taking their pleasure from rubber dreams and powdery phantasies. They were cushiony multimanmates, bewildered but willing, whom the strongest creatures would ride until their energies gave out, then dismount, and leave them gasping on the highways. Others had their sex organs only in their hands (these male again), and they used them only to beat and scarify the females they encountered who were unable, even in the fog, sufficiently to resemble the mothers of these males. Yet others mistook their sex organs for their hearts (which would lead to little local catastrophes); these would lie spread and bleeding in the paths of the busiest cavalcades, their spurting jism fueling the mardigras fog-fountains. And yet others mistook their hearts for sex organs, and stoked the furnaces of the more sentimental, binding sexual cults.*

*There were, too, amoeboids of all sexes, who formed and reformed their current shape according to the most recent stimuli into which they had collided. There were neutered casualties whose kicks came from goading others to sexual discharge to the point of extinction. There were whiplike rodents, snuffing forbidden fodder from the storerooms of the strong; there were ambulatory Muscles, which quacked and squeaked as they flexed on tottering feet, rippling and waving their fibres like cilia in the foetid breeze, persuading those already so-minded that the mutual exchange of such sights was Consummation. There were some stooped and humpy with sexual constipation, so picky were they about the places in-*

*to which they would shed their sexual load.*

*Some, unaware of the depths to which they had already sunk, sought dirtier depths from which to extract their masochistic spasms; others, maimed so long before that they had no memory of the mutilation, imagined that the sexual exercise was performed by some sort of sympathetic magic, as it were, and desperately nobbled others, talking, talking, talking them off. And whether they were tricky, ghoulish, furtive, or spongy, all fell victim to the stronger marauders: rogues who came looting, divesting them of their pathetic pelts, using them as fodder and bait for raids in a tougher territory.*

*And over the whole of the wide world only one Standard flew—its motto being that as there were no standards worth a damn, it was a free-for-all.*

*Fog-bound we may have been, but we were stubbornly Democratic.*

I did not inhabit those regions entirely, or I couldn't have survived. But I was helpless in the momentum of the fog; dependent on what eddied and flowed around me. Now and then, fortunately, almost an obbligato to my other murky activities, I would find myself beached on a mild, bright, sunshiny shore. I would stay there happy, porpoiselike in the soda-watery sexual surf, until the current carried me off again, into the thick of the fog.

The first surprise on hitting the homeland was to discover that, wherever I went, somehow I seemed to have offended every male I spoke to.

It took me about a year before I pinned down what was going wrong in any socio-sexual exchange.

Even then I didn't know why. I had only isolated *what*.

And *what* was this: there I would be happily chattering away, simply because it was, say, a party, and it was early-on chat-time; grinning and smiling and giving out sexual smoke-signals just as was my wont; or rather my will, habit, custom, whatever; and suddenly I would discover that I was being subtly, or not so subtly, insulted. Cold male eyes would flitter lizardlike over my body and find it lacked the cool and pasty proportions of the dollikins who stood emptily by, waiting to be filled. Or cold male eyes would look, and estimate, and gauge, and then lock shut, and I would find myself standing alone, in mid-flow. Or calculating male eyes would consider, and calculating males hands would maneuver, and then calculating male acid would bite into me, either verbally, or through a sound smack on the rear, and then calculating male would suddenly be doing his arithmetic somewhere else.

I hadn't been in England long when I was sent by the PRO of a firm I worked for to photograph an eminent sexologist, a friendly man given to making shocking and provocative statements about sex on television and in the popular press—statements which were curiously at odds, so lubricious were they, with his look of runty dryness. At the time I was in a blossoming of good looks. Maturing into the second half of my twenties, I was glossy haired, rounded slim, and had good eyes. No beauty queen you understand, but female, comely, and vigorous.

And recently made confident. Earlier that week I had been photographing a Miss World contest, and had been gazing wistfully at the unflawed fairy-dolls, wishing that I was as recognizable a desirable type as they, tired by all the put-downs of the English masculine stereotypes. I was watching when one of the judges, a Frenchman, with a huge, shiny forehead and soft eyes (I think he was one of the stringers from a local paper), came up to me, and said seriously, kindly, and softly into my ear: "Don't envy them. You are more beautiful than any of them." And moved off fast. One of those saving moments. For I thought: "In my own way, yes—it's the fools around me, the jerking vegetables with well-modulated voices who are simply *pretending* about me and my kind. That man was no fool. Bless him."

All women know themselves beautiful. All it needs is for the beauty to be called out of them, for the eye to see it and then it flowers; for the patch of ground in their beings where the feminine has its roots to be sunned and watered. *All women* know this, no matter how broken and brainwashed they are by the merchants touting the fairy-dolls: they know seriously and honestly where their beauty lies, as they know precisely, even lacking the experience, what true mating is.

So although I was no beauty queen, although I was getting diminishingly attractive, living as I did in a desert without food, water, sun, or nourishment in this respect, I still possessed the facility

to spot, even if discredited now and less frequently exercised, men with sexual intelligence.

Failing an encounter with one of those, I would
sit, an empty vessel, wondering what composite
of needs was to be projected onto me by each successive male.

Was I going to be moderately goodlooking, rat-
ing low on the middle register of the fairy-doll
scale, a commodity mete for stoking and poking
by a £1400-a-year man?

Was I going to be career woman, that unnatu-
ral species to be overexaggeratedly treated as a
male? Was I going to look to him predatory, on
the make, voracious, by virtue of my divorce and
my questioning eyes?

*Me* sat inside it all, watching the kaleidoscope
of projections, the muck dumped on me, amazed
and idiotic, stupidly undefended, wondering what
would be produced and hallucinated onto my
form by the specific alarms of each successive
male.

Elderly sexologist called out no one at all. He
did not, *could* not, as they say, Relate. He could
Perform, on the other hand, or so he said: never
stopped saying: embroidering on his remarkable
bedroom gymnastics, the physiological anomalies
that fascinated him, the chemical nerve-end firing
which he could deviously produce, the technical
requirements he demanded in sexual intercourse
between him and unnamed others. He discoursed
on the aphrodisiac properties of various scents, he
lectured me on the stimulating effects of tape-re-
corded noises and strategically placed mirrors; he
licked his lips and orated on the delights of two

women in his bed at once. I must give credit where due—he was very Advanced, trend-wise; for this, after all, was fifteen years ago.

But it was all rather as if he was trying to make it real by saying it; and he was, in addition, firing his words into some distant air in front of his own nose rather than at *me*.

I began to get the feeling that a doll, or painted android, would have done efficient service at lunch that day. It would have been much more efficient to have left the android sitting in, and bedded down myself with an old friend.

For sexologist was a member of the happy band of talkers; one of a species of mere Eye-Ballers.

# Chapter 9

Some Englishmen, I am now in the position to say after accumulated research into this type, feel alarmed if they look at a woman too directly, let alone have any too-direct *physical* contact with her. It makes it somehow too personal; too involving; gets them too close to that disconcerting, peculiar, distasteful, somehow *feminine*, quality about them.

Right through our lunch, with Dr. Zimmerman talking a blue pornographic streak, he would avert his gaze from mine—but take surreptitious, furtive glances in my direction periodically, photographing my image on his retina, then floating that image out in space a few inches in front of his eyes, and then watching that image intently through his pebble lenses instead of seeing the fleshy, palpable me. The photograph had no fixing agent, so when it faded he would be forced quickly to look at me long enough to take another snapshot, and bang it up on the airy wall in its place.

Never have I been dismantled, defused, filleted, and packaged quite so briskly. I must admit I was beginning to feel superfluous as the meal wore on. Dr. Zimmerman had something in common, certainly, with Ralph of the dirty talk. Except that Ralph strove for some response from me, and Zimmerman desperately avoided all chance of getting one. Uselessly, I tried to get a word in here and there, to make myself feel I was, in fact, present. But Zimmerman never drew breath. I had to fall back on an animated repertoire of grimaces: gee whizz, really, hm, how interesting, you surprise me; frown, cock head, slap thigh. Finally, I settled for a somber, brooding gaze.

We had just bounded, so to speak, through Levi's eighty-two gymnastic positions, the whole of the Kama Kalpa, and certain erotic witch rituals, me hanging breathlessly on to Zimmerman's word-tails while Zimmerman flew like a nymph on the momentum of his verbiage, when I suddenly thought: "Well, you never know, maybe you're wrong. Just because he is ignoring you, just because not one flinty spark is being struck through all this discourse, needn't mean he's totally dead." And chiefly because I was feeling mischievous, and also just because the subject under discussion was, after all—though I doubt if Zimmerman ever visualized what he was talking about—S-E-X, I thought: experiment. Find out. To do is to know.

Zimmerman was saying: "I wonder how you would look in some of the Indian love positions. You have the build and the look: you're the type.

An apsara. Your legs are long enough, if you're supple, you could try the position in which you leap up on the man and coil your legs . . ."

That triggered me. "Legs." OK. Here we go.

And I shifted my knee slightly so that my right leg touched Zimmerman's left; not aggressively, you understand, but gently, sweetly, moth-settlingly softly; not obvious, oh no.

Zimmerman reacted as if he had been branded. I could almost see the smoke and smell singed flesh. His leg leaped from mine the split second mine touched his; his left side flinched; his eyes rolled, his lips fleered.

But bravo for his frontal lobes, *they* were keenly in command. So dedicated and achieved an intellectual was he that in spite of his body's spasm of agitation his *sentence* majestically billowed on: ". . . and embrace him like a she-bear, neatly biting his left clavicle."

He glanced my way, fleetingly, as if to remind himself quickly who it was who had so importunately disturbed him. Oh, yes. Her. Nice, intelligent woman, brainy even, if you can keep her attention.

And he launched into the tale of his latest peculiar amour.


Things got somewhat farther with Richard, he who provided the next clue. Perhaps it was drink which took him there. For we *did* have action, and from my point of view (and I'm sure his too) some terrific action at that. It was *after* that, that the process of turning me into a phantom and phantasy began.

I must admit here that I have never been able to understand, though I have often been brow-beaten by, this business of the difference between the sexes. And don't jump to conclusions. I'm not talking doctrinal women's lib now.

What I mean is that really we're all *us,* aren't we? Some male, some female (thank goodness and *vive la différence)* but that this distinction is already secondary. First comes the ordinary human connection.

I met Richard at a hilarious party, given after the opening of his art exhibition. He was getting famous. I found myself next to him at a meal. Later that night, we laughed at each other's jokes uproariously, heartily, gazed drunkenly into each other's eyes with alternating speculation and amusement, and then went home together and straight to bed.

And we had a *lovely* time.

We were both a bit drunk (he probably far more than I) and had that easy, unthinking sexual connection where we slid from one move and mode to another, lightly anticipating each other's sensual needs, the requirement of the one body drawing the finger or mouth or breath or organ of the other to the precise spot which at that moment sought it; our bodies moving and flowing soap-smooth from one body attitude to the next. We met, searched, glowed and sparked; we joined, and abdicated our will to our body's will, for our bodies were not strangers but old companions; laughing, sensitive, ministering companions; deft, light, concerned friends. My mind went into the

soft black dark, and let the old knowing places of
my body relax and melt into the surfaces of Richard's body; my mind ceased questioning and my
body made the search into Richard's recesses and
skin secrets. We made comfortable, satisfying love,
which paced itself with sureness, and rose, when
we least expected, to an intense, bright rocket-rip
and flash of satisfaction.

We lay together, he still inside me, and talked
fondly like the old friends we seemed to be, and
then made love again, urgent and passionately
this time—as if we had been through the first sig-
nifying encounter, established our good faith, and
could now risk, between us, the kind of abandonment of body or mind protection and could push
and urge and taunt and trick and haul and carry
and fly on the back of and be flown on the back
of and somehow carry each other to a region of
fusion—whether physical or mental now was indistinguishable—to which neither of us before had
traveled, and enter its deep black newness together, into the vast and gasping silence and space.

Both of us were amazed.

At dawn Richard left me.

He had to—he was married.

I went to sleep instantly, and awoke, cheerful,
knowing I had a new boyfriend. I had, at the
time, absolutely no encumbrances. I lived alone.
There were plenty of cuddling friends, and a few
arid go-nowheres, but the confirmation of the kind
that had happened between Richard and me the
night before was of an order so different from anything in the fog, or even from anything in the

glowworm nesting sexing, which gave me a vital
and basic food, that even had I been carrying the
responsibilities of home and giant family, the join-
ing between us would have had to be acknowl-
edged as of a special order—to be or not to
be repeated, but certainly not to be altered or di-
minished in assessment or by, so to speak, lit crit.
But it looked as if it might grow into something,
for at the party the night before I'd watched
Richard with his wife, and as far as I could see I
wouldn't be interfering with a thing.

So I whistled and skipped my way through the
day, happily waiting for Richard to telephone. I
was still sufficiently new in England to assume
that the way we did things at home was the way
they did them here. Cultural assumptions of this
kind are dangerous. At home, after such a nice
sexy evening, let alone after a real happening, so
to speak, the form was straightforward. The man
would phone the following day merely to make
some confirmatory comment, to exchange voice
sound, and to fix up the principle—if not the moment—that we should at some point see each other again. No problem could come up that I could
foresee. Sex between Richard and me confirmed
a natural harmoniousness between us. That done,
we could get to know each other, in whatever form that would take.

As the *I Ching* would put it: no blame. Richard
did what it was in him to do—but he sure must
be a victim of the English Syndrome. He didn't
telephone all that day, nor did he get in touch for
nearly a week. Then he simply rang, and said in
a glum, portentous voice only:

"I must see you. Can I come round?"

"Sure. Lovely. How've you been?"

"Er . . . I'll come round."

His first words on coming round were: "I've come to give you up."

Bafflement on my part: "You can't give me up. You haven't got me yet."

"Well, I can't see you again."

"Why not?"

He burst out with some violence: "You are the sort of woman I need in my life. I want to be married to you. I should have married you. You are everything I wish for and dream of. And if I can't have all of you . . . then I want none of you."

Very good for the ego. I said mildly, with the kind of realism unwanted at such moments: "Well, why don't you get to know me better? You may not think the same way when you do. Let's just take it step by step, and see what happens."

He shook his head; and in the heaviness which clung on him, weighting his shoulders and leadening his speech, I realized that he was despairing of my ever understanding.

But I think I understood only too well. Richard had done a version of the Dr. Zimmerman's. After he had left my bed he had spent six long days with me—in his head. We had made love, we had passionate, romantic, creative, and fruitful episodes, we had tormented each other and urged each other on to new personal heights, the way we had in bed that night.

In his mind, he had traveled years away from the point in ordinary time where we had met.

And when he reached the end of the mental

journey the distance between the two so appalled him that he found the journey in reality impossible to begin.

And so the great renunciation scene.

I was very sad.

# Chapter 10

It is this kind of sex-in-the-head that I found the most stultifying aspect of what has happened to the poor Englishman. On another occasion, I went down to the country to a house party with two high-born English males as hosts. Arrived to find that none of the other guests had showed. In my former culture that would have meant only one thing. Like dirty Dick in my teens, it was rapine or seduction, and take your choice. But with these two arid Etonians, the defection of the friends was social on the friends' part, I should think, rather than calculated on the part of the duffer brothers. The friends simply knew it would be dull, and at the last moment cried off.

So there we were, the three of us, in an elegant country seat, and for one whole weekend I was treated as these men probably had treated their fags at school—as a kind of second-class being, to be teased and overlooked, unless I made the right blah-blah formula noises that would have pressed their buttons. But the formula was well known to me and dull.

All I needed to do would have been to behave like the unapproachable idolized female-figure crystalized in the psyche of many Englishmen: the granite goddess, she so nailhard and glinty that many mistake her for Diamond. Her combination is, in varying proportions: a dash of Mum, a touch of Bitch, a shaking of Exotic, a wiff of eau de cologne, a tease of curling secret hair, and a twist of uncomprehending silliness.

Given a dose of that, and the brothers would have been quivering with delight. Clever women in other ages have known this and used it. But times have changed. I was my own mistress, and intended to stay that way—until and unless the job came along which offered perks of some magnificence.

It was, in some ways, a hilarious weekend. Duffer-brother-the-first gave me cooking to do, then hovered in the kitchen in case I should smash anything. He even winced when I attacked the leeks with some ferocity.

Duffer-brother-two took me walking over survival course terrain, and then jeered and scoffed when I lagged behind, handicapped by natural inability, bad footgear, and rage.

They were also such a *sentimental* pair. Unable to distinguish beauty from sugar at all levels, their confusion generalized, permeating many other things. One of the brothers went weak-eyed one evening at the sight of a majestic sunset. "Look how beautiful. Look," he urged, on the verge of collapse, knees wobbling, voice lurching with emotion. I took a quick, unwilling squint through his eyes in order to see what he saw; and the sight, through his eyes, was something so tepidly pretty that it wasn't worth having the collywobbles over. Perhaps he was stirred in his depths. In that case he should have left the sensation *there,* where it happened; for it was something horribly watered down which plinked out by the time he had surfaced it into expression. I couldn't bear to be effulgent about the sunset with him; it would have been compounding the insult to the sun. I pretended I hadn't heard, and continued walking, thereby committing a solecism: I was not Sensitive.

Trying to do something to make the longer winter nights by the fire pass, I would entertain them with stories, with conceits and delights, with surprises, with sheer *energy,* and they would laugh and wait for more, but not really contribute anything. I think they thought their very presence was gift enough. And an ordinary person-girl, as opposed to their female ideal, didn't really warrant the courtesy of wooing—or even the courtesy of acknowledgment as female, as a common civil gesture to good social relations—that one of the other type would elicit by their mere presence and the duffer brothers' conditioning. I just needed ordinary lubrication, socially speaking, and not much at that. Just a soupçon of emotion, of mundane human flow and ease, a touch of lightness. They had none to spare.

They treasured their horde of emotion, so unknown was its nature to them, as a rare and vital commodity: not to be handed out to strangers indiscriminately (not just a *little?* you're damn right, NOT) although perhaps cashed in and sacrificed on the altar of their special unreachable Fantasy Made Flesh.

I discovered about the granite goddess and the attendant difficulties of those brought up in her service because to offlay my boredom I used the weekend for research. I questioned the duffer brothers closely about their childhoods, their backgrounds, their families. Stiffly they began to talk, finding it surprisingly difficult to remember their sensitive sapling days, and for the first hour, very unwilling as well.

They were like the many Englishmen who hate to be touched, say, in a massage. Sex touching is all right because they know what that is: that's dirty old sex, and it's allowed. But this lovely, releasing, fluttering, kneading one-way pleasure, spreading lines of comfort along the body and not lassoed to the sex organs, what's this? Too difficult and disturbing, this. It must be wrong, it's happening in the drawing room. These feelings are reserved for smelly old sexbeds. Massage to them is like alcohol in some cultures: to be enjoyed—only if you can justify it with suitable medicinal reasons.

But after sufficient time, when it finally dawns on them that there is no trace of well, *anything*, in the mind of the other except that this is a pleasant and natural form of behavior, they find it delicious.

Touch and talk for the tightly buttoned British comes slow, but when it comes, the dam breaks.

From the duffer brothers I gathered the first material which informed me about the malady that has shaped, or rather whittled, so many highborn elegant English—appalling qualities to find in anyone, worse when one remembers that they Run Our Lives. For though they put it in halting, stumbling, personal terms, this, essentially, is the story they told.

## TALE OF THE GRANITE GODDESS AND THE PETRIFIED TITMICE

*Once upon a time, in the history of every titmouse, there was a wonderful era when he was not a titmouse, but a Crystal Boy, and he lived in happiness with his Own True Mother, who was a beautiful Diamond Lady.*

*That was before the terrible things happened. We think, though there are many different theories, that she must have been taken away by the Nanny-Woman, who in her place put a still-beautiful Granite Goddess, who looked just like our mother. Others think that it always was our mother, but that something happened to Us, so that we saw her now as Granite, and the Diamond flashed out at us only occasionally.*

*This is what we think. We can't be clear about the next bit, because it is painful and confused* in our memories. But we think that the change into titmice began then too, though we do know it was a long process.

Our granite Goddess was strange and beautiful and inaccessible. Sometimes she was grainy and flashing, and we feared her. At other treasured moments we remember her, winking radiant, soft-centred of breast and nacreous of neck, even welcoming. At those moments, though we knew the ultimate pain involved, we would melt onto her flinty, glinty hardness, wishing she could melt too, as sometimes, in the dimly remembered, she had done.

At special moments we would come to her: for a bedtime kiss, where we would attempt our longed-for outpourings, before she twinkled off to her ceremonies with the other gods and goddesses.

It was all very puzzling, because we knew she was Ours, most particularly—and yet she wasn't. Perhaps she couldn't cuddle and hold in a way that was also a hardship to her? For she was all scintilla and spangle; the fairy on the Christmas tree; her brilliance edged, knife sharp.

She had other mysterious powers which were never spoken of. But we discovered. Once we saw, after creeping to the forbidden temple, and the memory binds us still, that she and Father, their masks removed, disrobed after their rituals and ceremonies, had another monstrous ceremonial together; a secret, mysterious symbiosis.

It scared us, but burns still in our memories as the desirable extinction we yearn for ourselves.

*For in spite of the fearsomeness of the scene, we must admit that Father looked blissful. We think it must have been some ancient mystery play called, perhaps, "Now I Eat You." Both had altered fearfully; one shrunk, the other gigantic; hardly, now, Our Parents, but mad memory ghouls from our worst dreams. The female's mouth, as we gazed, was no ordinary chopper, but a stony snake-mouth, inside of which she held Father, or rather, Father rested, as if she had gobbled him all up a long time before, and had left, for appearance' sake, lolling from her lips, an arm feebly to flap and an eye watery to see and a lock of hair to represent strength. She looked engorged, mountainously replete, as if stoking her granite powers during this rigid, throbbing conjunction.*

*And Father? He looked happy in an enigmatic way.*

*We knew that the world of our demigods would one day be ours to inherit, but we lacked instruction. In the meantime, we were timid little titmice, coming when called, flashing our crystal only in fugitive summer moments, in the rose garden or among the peaches, alone.*

*There was a fall, and a gap, and a puzzle. For we were given into the keeping of a second aspect of our Goddess, Nanny-Woman. Or was it she, Scabby-Nanny, who was responsible for the Terrible Change? This, too, remains a puzzle.*

*For Nan often made life very nice, really.*

And yet, she was the Enemy. She cuddled and hugged us in a way our mother was kept from; she comforted us in our pain, and stayed with us in our loneliness, and wheedled and bossed and joked and punished and gave us warmth and bad times and years of care.

She did the unforgivable.

She Won our Hearts.

But our hearts belonged to Mummy, really. Nanny often told us so.

Which made a further puzzle, you see.

Nanny was new bread and chilblains and quarrels and warm bathrooms and a guardian from storms and a tyrannical slut. What we experienced in her dispensation must have been of a lower grade than the mysteries withheld by Mother.

All the Evidence showed us. Mother was High Priestess of this Female-Divided: Remote, Beautiful, Longed-For, with Power of Life and Death. Nan was Bountiful, of course, but it was only her beauty (sorry, we meant to say Duty) to be. It was her day-to-day job, and she did it; we could rely on it. But Mother . . . ah, she could not be relied on. She haunted our dreams.

The everyday comfort of Nan was our life on the trivial plane. It was really not very valuable. We got it every day, which makes it ordinary. And she only gave it because it was her Job.

Mother paid her.

With MONEY.

So she wasn't ours, axiomatically.

She was free to leave. And one day she did.

*And we found ourselves disquietingly ill for no apparent reason.*

*This is what we have learned about love and women.*

*Our story.*

## Chapter 11

After the transformation had already taken place, and they were little titmice, a new epoch began. Clear-eyed, flower faced, piping-treble, precocious and braced, they grew up in the worship of the Goddess of the Cleft-in-Twain.

The twain became, predictably, their stereotypes.

The uncomfortable, unreachable, magical She, who left traces of her cologne lingering in the corridors of longing. And the slutty-rutty, bed-and-bawd usurper, provider of ordinary rough comfort for a Price; the adored social inferior, for the hide-and-seek of the everyday, but never for Society, or for Sundays. Surely the fact that she never ate food, broke bread, at the table of her Goddess-Sister, made her relative position apparent without question.

Once I even heard a real-life Nanny say it. "The

hardest part of my job?" she beamed. "Oh that's an *easy* one to answer. You've got somehow to make the children understand that it's their Mummy they love, not you."

It was so, it consequently falls out, that the avid little titmice learned their lines.

What they felt for Bitch-Grainy was love?

Right. That feeling is Love. That amalgam of longing, and hurt, and pain, and fright, and sexual horror and incest hope, is Love.

Right.

Love.

With that straight, we can proceed. What, then do we feel for Nan? Something nameless, but surely less respectable.

Love has already been allocated.

Goddess glinty, Goddess hard-as-rock, unyielding in her purposes, does what is Best for her titmice, her Walled-Up crystal boys. To those ends she sends them, fresh and chilly, into a specially graven cold-storage center known as—you guessed —the Public School. Here there are no females to melt the ice. The only Feminine to Hand, to coin a phrase, is that Aspect in the other little boys. Female Memory, as indeed Crystal Memory, continues in Titmouse Memory, remote and remarkable, and is burnished by glitty visits to sports days and prize-givings, when duty is done and acolytes bust their guts for her smile, as they breast the race tapes.

Nothing could melt in this icy training-cage.

The goods were contracted to go back in the same condition, intrinsically, in which they arrived, decorated up a bit by the gloss of learning and an ornament of style. But with everyone withholding warmth and flow, with so much denial, so much unsureness and hurt, with so complete a palimpsest of pleasures overlaying cornered hopes, it could have set the place awash and sunk it, had the tide turned and the waves broke.

So they froze, our little titmice, a whole nation and generation of titmice, and learned (instead of the Nanny-trivialities of how to Be and how to Give and what you Feel) how to Be . . . leaders of men, and how to Give . . . orders to others, and what to Feel . . . in the name of responsibility and importance—postures in which the lacks would not show, and from which could be administered empires—vast and farflung in the earlier days, currently shrunk and restricted to special fields of enterprise.

But wherever they found themselves in a variety of territories peopled by Messy Others, the titmice would not be Tainted—because they had superior minds in refrigerated bodies.

They came out as frozen as they went in. Ten years passed, but the cool blue eyes and the fresh skin and the impudent good manners and the unmarked faces, held rigid and waiting for experience of the heart, these had never moved, softened, or been touched.

The longer they were not, the more protected the ice-wall became, from which the small boy could shoot his guns. Defend. Defend. Attack as Defense. Rip and Tear. And sigh for Mum.

Some, so the duffer brothers made clear, never came to life again.

And that is the story of why the privileged Englishman looks younger than his years.

He is.

Is it any wonder they dislike women like me? We sluts?

Is it any surprise that one of them could weep to me one midnight, breaking his heart as his tether snapped, and he opened up, dragging the statement from his depths, ashamed, but prepared to risk the question now, to win or lose all: "Why" . . . he cried out, "Why? Why did nature do it? I have never understood . . . just why . . ."—he faltered, spitting the words out singly—"*why* did Nature have to arrange it so that *the two holes were so close together?*"

It would have been more fitting; so to speak, if Nan and Mum had kept their distance, even there.

He also seemed to feel that the enormity was somehow my fault. He led me to understand that Granite Goddess's plumbing arrangements (like Superman's true love, who was a Mermaid) presented no problems.

Natch.

Granite Goddess never loses her power, for she holds fast at the root which never grew—the infantalized core of unsatisfied yearning. In this way, as do any personalities abusing power in any human sphere, she keeps her subjects satellite around her, unable either to consummate or go free.

The little crystal boys, the little titmice, fasten on to those females plastic and formless enough to hold their longings for the Granite Goddess. And the females have been subjected too—mistress and master prisoner together—in a wordless, binding, steel-structured initiation; they have been fed the Goddess ways.

So they posture and beckon and cold-shoulder and toss their heads, and the little titmice, petrified, watch their own machinery rolling into action, responding, as salivating dogs do, to the stimuli from these vapid creatures, who know how to extract devotion, duty, wedlock, and will—but who remain ignorant until too late of the true nature of any of them.

The great pity is, that blinded by tears and fright, titmice divide the world into two. If you're not one, you must be the other.

Sluts are for fucking. Nanny-snatch is meat and potatoes, so to speak. Goddesses are for feasts—though it turns out that there is one constant dish-of-the-day: tasty little titmice.

Thus the zombie dance, English style.

And the further pity is that the plastic females can be awakened, and the titmice regain their crystal, if it is not left too late; if they have avoided doing too much damage (like savaging such as me) while the rescuers are kitting up nearby. For there *are* surrogates for Granite Goddesses which do, in the end, produce workable solutions. This truth I now offer to all social workers and ministrators in the sexual field. The solution lies in Substitution—an Exotic Foreign Woman, most usually, in whom the titmouse initially mistakes a different set of cultural signals, plus trouble with the language, for basal idiocy. The girl resorts to blank looks, patient emptiness, noticeable sexiness, as the only available *lingua franca*.

The crystal boy who gets one of these may be in luck—she will probably thaw him out. In the same way as Arne and I broke through many halts and barriers in a flash because we were such unexpected kinds, each to the other, so too here—so beyond the realms of ordinary experience can Goddess and Nan fuse; sex and sweetness and longing and breakfast and bliss and summonses all have place together.

Like in all self-fulfilling prophesies, crystal boys turn their empty, plastic flower-girls into Goddesses, not to be approached too closely; to be kept for the dinner table and high social rituals; to be appeased and placated.

But these poor goddesses, stuck up on their pedestals, finally cannibalize their mates only because there's not much other food around. "I am not like this," the sleeping girl inside them might try to speak out and say. "Yes you are," says the man, her victim, firmly—hoping to keep the flaps of his world pegged down against the caprices and tornadoes of reality.

Because their men don't really like them, the women can only suspend animation and reflect back a mirror of their men's needs. And similarly, it may require a man from foreign parts to light their fires.

This I have watched: English women smouldering and basking in the admiration of the men in, say, Italy or Greece. Women of all shapes, builds, temperaments, styles. The male eye, the male appreciation, in street, in sudden encounter, animates them. It is so deeply buried in them, so armored against the contempt and fear of their males, that until their trust is won they are convinced that these other men are *making fun* of them! Then they, too, awaken—and some of them never come home again.

Some silly academic fool even tried it out in the field, so to speak; half joke, half pissological experiment. I found it seriously written up in an academic report. The young men of his university class were told to flatter and pay attention to the plainest girl of the group. The assumption of the law-and-ordering behavioral psychologist was that she just might begin to behave as if she were really attractive. Fool. What criminal lack of courtesy: as if he shouldn't bone-and-body know that this is all it takes.

The girl flowered.

By the end of the year she *was* the most attractive girl in class.

But I know men. They were probably puzzled. Somewhere those who had been in on the deception would have "known," in all their conditioned responses which feel so disarmingly like true knowledge, that—even though by now fascinated by her—would have known that she wasn't really attractive; not really. Bright and blossomed she may have become, but she wouldn't have had the lineaments of the Man-eater, the Granite Goddess, would she? She would have suffered from malnutrition once, and so would have flowered into something different, more her own.

She would have been too uncomfortably human.

# Chapter 12

Flesh-and-blood ladies have a hard time with the crystal boys. For these children are capable of enormities, without ever losing their self-esteem (except when it rears up in the terrors of midnight) or even knowing what they've done: the way an alien might brush roughly past a flower, and not know; or the way an alien might tramp through a forcefield wearing a leaden shield, and then claim he didn't feel a thing, so there couldn't have been anything there.

Once I had a nasty dental operation, and a middle-aged titmouse, a posh professor, full of decorations and upper-class twangings and pleasures, loudmouthed and self-satisfied, seemingly shaped by the Edwardians even in the mid-sixties, kindly offered to fetch me from the hospital and bring me home.

I'd known him for some months. My only rich Australian relative, an uncle, had met him when he was lecturing there and asked him to look me up on his return. He'd liked what—rather than who—he'd found, and came calling from time to time, when it suited him. I made him randy as hell, and by now was using this power, heartily and maliciously, whenever I saw there was something to be gained. In the fog, you use what weapons you've got.

Prof had a Granite Goddess wife, mini-variety (academics until recently always had to make do with shabby versions of this breed though this is changing now, as lady intellectuals read the fashion pages and learn how to do themselves up, as a branch of expertise rather than sex) and I represented to him, so he said, "Enthusiasm," which he told me—me having no classics, which was a charming lack, but a lack nonetheless—was a classic Greek virtue in its original Greek meaning, whatever that was.

I took his cultivated word for it. From what he said about his wife (who of *course* didn't understand him) it was clear that they were both having a rotten time in bed, but the impression I got was that Prof was something like a conceited Jeffrey, and had only himself to blame. Jeffrey, too, thought only of himself; he was content to be alone in bed with a handy hole. But Prof was so booted-up with self-congratulation that he also demanded the feedback that he was a wow of a lover.

"It's so sordid between us," he told me musically, waywardly. "She never moves. And then right at the end, as a gesture, she opens her legs and throws back her head and shouts 'buttocks and bums and arses and cunts,' and that's it."

Clearly, it wasn't enough for his wild energies, her sexual tally-ho. He was massively built, and always on the go. He expended some of his energy in ferocious academic disputes, demoniacal territorial vendettas on behalf of the ideas he considered his own, and energetic sorties to foreign parts to do his strange research (he was, of all things, a botanist), where he would no doubt fuck the unresisting local girls on the mountain slopes, wondering all the while why his pale bogey-wife, locked away in her academic box, couldn't see to the meals and mend the clothes and impress his superiors with her brightness, preside over tea parties, *and* do this kind of thing come nightfall.

With all this he still had energy left to dash to London to see me, when he had a couple of hours free.

And why did I see him? Well, for one thing, he was massive and muscular, and I liked his looks. For another, while he was searching for an Enthusiastic Amateur, I was looking for a Bed Rock: security from a stable older person, and confirmation of my social decency from a respected member of society.

And while his chief disappointment in me was probably that I invariably took his wife's side when he complained about her (Christ, I would have behaved far worse in the situation he described), mine in him was that Status Figures, dammit, shouldn't behave like schoolboys when the lights go off in the cinema, and shove their hands up your twat, especially not when those hands have shaken the hand of the Queen.

Like a schoolboy, however, he was normally quite manageable. I simply reached idly for a few Granite Goddess tricks, and they worked each time.

Almost.

For I was, after all, a youngish slut-type. If not on my guard, I was fair game. If arses and cunts were too salty for his elegant sensibilities, then that applied only in the clean realms of his family sanctity. Me he fetched from the dental clinic, all blood-smelling where my tooth was bleeding, reeling from the anesthetic, which I had not taken well, puffy from weeping (I had sobbed my heart out while coming round) and pointed the car in the right direction for my flat, but then at the last moment veered off toward Wimbledon Common, and pulled open my blouse and drove his teeth into my neck and in the same wrenching movement got his toy soldier out and tried to stick it in my sentry-box.

Thus the greater thinker and humanitarian.

Perhaps *his* Nanny had been all fright: a walking broth of pyorrhea, false teeth, and oedema of the face?

The worst thing, self-evidently, about a fog is that one cannot *see*. And the worst of this for women—I have no idea how bad it is for men— is that one is mistaken for so many different stereotypes, and treated accordingly. And often, out of sheer loneliness, or the wish for the goodies which will be handed out by acquiescing, we say, from time to time, all right, consider me like this.

Once a tall, bony, sensitive Englishman mistook me for a Granite Goddess, nudged along by me. I was doing well at the time in my job, and could afford the necessary fancy dress, which on its own was almost enough to do the trick. He adored me. He gave me charming and imaginative presents. On one occasion he returned from Holland with two ruddy, bright, tropical birds, cooing and nuzzling, downy in their gilded cage.

It was a restful, if not, as they say, meaningful, relationship. Our meetings were periodic and *structured*, by which I mean that they had a fixed starting time and a ritual progression, and so I had time, between appointments, to get myself dolled-up Goddess-wise, to relax at the hairdresser, take time with my makeup, and transform myself into the dish to be served up. It made a change from my sloppy, scutty, practical daytimes, coping alone and often with difficulty in the daily bash-through.

After the restaurant (I hadn't eaten so well in months) or after the theater (nor sat in such posh seats), he would adore me in his particular way. I can see why Englishmen's trophy-wives need time and cash and servants: for this sort of man you must *always* smell sweet, your skin be oil-smooth, your crevices antiseptic.

So I became this receptive confectionery, and he relished me like a sweetmeat, making love to me with a concentrated ardor which was almost intellectually planned, and almost boylike in its overwhelmed sensitivity. I abandoned myself to his worship, finding that his mouth and fingers traveled me tremblingly; fish-tender mouth, spider-walking fingers; he, and I, appreciating, savoring.

This is how the British take their tender lustings on their own kind. It had never happened to me before. I read from his demeanor that he wanted me passive, abandoned to his ministrations. I found his procedures delicious, piercing; peach-sweet: through the very restraint involved.

Sometimes I would tease him with a petulant, bright bitchiness; a five-year-old's tease: light, but deadly; soft but spot-on, coming as it does from a mind which perceives and has no axe to grind, nothing it values that it needs to connive at to gain. He loved that too: it excited him when I would turn away from his gaze, indifferent and captious.

We did not make love often—not each time we saw each other. And this, for me, was also a new experience. If dinner or theater was late, he took me home—because we both worked the next day, and the setting would have been marred by haste.

In spite of our intimacies, Jason seemed timid with me—although bold and sure in his masculine world where he built buildings and commanded respect.

He warmed, at first, with great sweetness, when I responded instantly to his sensitive searching round my body's charted pleasure points; so sensitive that the bays, peaks, inlets and coastlines of pleasure became more painstakingly mapped; more frequent; placed closer on my skin. But he had only one mode, and this was it—and in time I found it difficult.

Greedy me was many things, responsive to mood, weather, and season. Sighing Jason was but one.

After keeping myself sheathed, as it were, for several weeks, tamping down the energy which rose at his touch, I one night forgot myself. A wave of capriciousness and female power gripped me while he was loving me, and I drew draughts of female knowledge, and spread and grew and lay over him and then sat and proudly showed myself.

That was the first night our rhythm broke. He managed to turn me over again, and then rode me, buffeting angrily, grown aggressively out of his usual penetrating timed-and-sensed slow thrusts.

But he could not ride to his destination.

He became rougher and angrier, then frustrated, then utterly depressed. Nor did he want to talk or be comforted.

I had broken the rules.

We continued to see each other, but the outgoings, not the innings, were now the focus of our contact, and the occasions on which we both needed early nights increased. His physical coldness became, within the space of five meetings, a rigid aversion for my touch and gaze.

To compensate for this, because we both enjoyed each other's company, the material we presented to each other for talk, interest, investigation, and consideration, so to speak, grew and flourished.

There were painful nights, when I wanted loving and he would pretend not to see my need and drop me, like a boy on his first date, at my doorstep, with a formal "thank you" for the nice night out. On one occasion I yelled at him like a harridan, and told him exactly what I thought of his shrinking distaste, but he shrank further, wilting on the instant, and I felt a twist of pain at what I'd done, and when we met again we both pretended it hadn't happened.

Within a few months we discovered that we had somehow established a holding link. The psychological stickiness that had oozed from us through the pain of our adjustment into the different relationship now bound us. We were friends. We are friends still. When enough time had passed, and wounds had turned to scars, he was forthright enough to answer my questions.

"What went wrong?" I asked.

"Oh," he said. "I couldn't go on like that. I was getting quite wrong."

"How do you mean, wrong?"

He hesitated.

"Go on. We've been through so much anyway. Tell me."

"Well, for one thing, you *came* too easily. There was no challenge. No problem to solve."

In my research moods, when they come over me, I never defend myself or get into arguments. I ask the questions. So storing that one for later consideration, I continued: "Anything else?"

"Yes. You were too much *there*. Your eyes were always on me. You became a *person*."

As he spoke, he was suddenly back in that mode of emotion: petulant, disgusted.

We were drinking old armagnac by his fire, talking in murmurs, lines of understanding opening out from our buzzy sounds.

"Do you think it could have been different, Jason? We seem very right for each other now, as companions. And at the beginning it was so good. Could we try going to bed again, do you think?"

"No," he said, instantly remote, but with a combination, in his need to wound slutty me, of his saving, right honesty. "Not once we became friends. With me, the other thing is always over then.

"I'm happiest, really, with black girls."

## Chapter 13

I was cured of envying goddesses finally by knowing Penny. Through her I saw that the story —any story, in fact—can happen any way round: beginnings, middles, and ends need not occur in that order.

There but for the grace of, goes she in my place and I in hers. The stereotypes aren't the result of inherent talent or deficiency, but of shaping and distortion. Beautiful girls are like the boonzai trees. They are forced and altered by circumstance or desire, and then their new shape becomes so familiar that what is learned behavior begins to feel like nature, both to the girl herself and those who see her.

Boonzai trees, however, are the result of knowledge and art.

We have some random forces altering us.

I learned all this from Penny. She was a broken fairy-doll; a goddess resculpted, reshaped (reformed is how the conventional world put it, moralistic and gratified), and then tossed away.

### THE STORY OF PRETTY PENNY, WHO BECAME PLAIN PENNY, AND THEN POTTY PENNY

Once upon a time, nearly thirty years ago, there was a little girl called Penny. Nobody was interested in her particularly, for about fifteen years. By then, pale, pretty, and frail; blue-eyed, with a head set straight and high on narrow shoulders, she was reedlike, golden, delicate; a lovely meadow buttercup.

This being a consumer society, she was automatically reached for as she ripened. Her uncle, in whose house she had lived after her parents died, was found by her aunt while he was trying, one day, to lick the fresh yellow butter from the cup.

Auntie sent Penny away. Untrained; dreamy but determined; she sleepwalked to the particular marketplace where the glitter and prizes for the have-nots are dangled. She became a stripper.

She was not beautiful. She was too watery-light, too slack, almost, for that. When she met me, both her face and body still offered the blank and undifferentiated spaces onto which the contemporary preferred signals of beauty could be inscribed. She had soft, child-smooth skin, as if she had one epidermal layer too little; like velvet to touch; like silk to see. Only her mouth showed the strain. It was too thin; too carefully held; it had no pulse in it.

She met both Simon and me when she was working, after strenuous but docile years, in an expensive strip-club in Mayfair. At twenty-six her pale eyes had watched a great range of human behavior as it staggered, tossed, dribbled, leaked, and warred its way through her thighs; letting them come; scooping off the gifts and comforts; never a prostitute but taking as dues, money, flats, attention, and desire.

"It was quite a good life," she once told me reflectively. "I mean I never *minded.* I just did what they wanted and let them imagine what they liked. It was all the same to me, really."

We compared notes once. It turned out that soft-voiced Penny had never had the same sense as I that her *self* had somehow got lost; that the remaining vestige, the last gleam of light was the lost Necessity to which all life was geared.

I had to find the place where everything happened in the light; collect sufficient light-beads to thread a stepping-path back to the source of the brightness. Penny, on the other hand, never felt that. In some ways her sense of self had never been disrupted or disturbed; it was utterly unconscious, looking after its own needs, and leaving the Penny-of-the-world to look after hers. Penny's focus was different; on the things *she* had lost: the family she had never quite belonged to; the security she craved.

Things which would have ruined me, broken me apart, smashed me in splinters, bounced right off her, making no dent. In this she too (as I), still was essentially Virgin. Deed done, but not known to be done, and therefore not done. A pantomime was all that had been managed. And certain experiences are like Justice, *not* really done until they are "seen," really understood and digested. Penny had chewed her way through a variety of rotten fruit, as had I, but had never swallowed the apple that would have opened her eyes.

Thus it was that she had taken part in orgies, flagellation scenes, dress-up scenes, and sexual charades without really caring too much. The way she described those scenes, it became clear that glittered up with excitement and alcohol, legions of businessmen thought they were having a whale of a time. But the highlife was just Penny and some of her mates laying in stocks against a rainy day.

When she met Simon, she was longing just to have one man; for someone to say to her: "be for me only."

"But I didn't think it would be someone as terrific as him," she told me. "Goodlooking, rich, everything—a real man-of-the-world type. He had traveled a lot and he was, well, you could see he was used to getting his own way. I like that in a man.

"Of course, dear, it goes without saying that if he hadn't been rich, the whole thing may have been different. But he was a property millionaire, so that was OK too."

"Did he make a pass at you right off, or what?" I asked, intrigued about the forbidden territories into which I could never get by on my looks. Penny was a glowing buttercup. I was merely a rackety rose.

"Well, you know, when the show's over, how

you go into the club and sit about. He asked me to join his party, and there were about eight people there. He didn't have a girl with him, so I sort of evened up the numbers.

"Everyone told me afterward that he's a very brainy man, but I liked him right off that night because he was funny and sexy. He really was. And very nice to me. Not like those idiots who feel they own you because you work at the club and they're the customers; who handle you like shoddy goods.

"And I really liked his looks. He was built big, like a sailor. I like that, because I'm so little maybe. And he was the right age, just about forty. You know, Annie, I sat there wishing I could have a man like that for my own.

"You know the sort of person who makes everyone enjoy themselves? Except that every now and then someone would irritate him and then he'd straightway insult them and turn away as if they weren't there any more. He upset a lot of people, I know."

"Mm. He doesn't suffer fools gladly," I said.

"Oh, there you go," said Penny with a trace of irritation. "Always people like to put words in my mouth. He suffered *me* gladly enough. It wasn't all sex, by any means, though there was a lot of that too."

"Was he straight?" I asked curiously.

"Oh, yes. He just liked it a lot. So we made love in three-somes and even more quite often, and we saw blue films and once he hired a photographer and we made one, and we watched ourselves in mirrors, and I had a load of different clothes he liked me to wear, and sometimes he made me tell him in (she giggled) *words*, exactly what he was doing to me."

"I had one like that too," I said reminiscently. "A Roman Catholic. Very strict. He was also a very nice guy. Terrific. I really liked him. But he too. Come the crunch and he'd always say: 'Tell me what I'm doing to you.' And I'd say: 'You're fucking me.' And then he'd say: 'Tell me where your legs are. And tell me what you want me to do now.' It drove him wild. But I used to get a bit uncomfortable."

"Me too. But still. Nothing's perfect. Maybe it's a kink some of the decent guys have. I've known much worse."

Penny made it clear that if that had been all Simon had asked her to tell him, she might have survived.

"After all, men are like that, aren't they? But the trouble was he wanted to know all about *me*, too. Not in bed, of course, but at other times. Well, you know. I didn't used to like getting all those things mixed up. Because honestly, if a person behaves like that it's too much, too nice, I suppose. It's like what I really want, you know? Someone I can talk to; who's also interested in me daytime.

"He found out all about me because he kept asking questions as if he really wanted to know the answers. I didn't tell him everything at once, he had to drag it out, because—I'll tell you something—in spite of what they say they don't really want that even though they say they do. Don't tell them everything, keep them guessing.

They get curious and they come around more and more trying to find out.

"He had this streak which after I got used to it would get me going too. I had to tell him how it was with other men. Sometimes even do it with other men, with him watching."

"Didn't you mind?"

"Not really. It was quite fun sometimes."

That was Penny. No great hopes. Quite fun. Rather nice. Not bad. Her accolades.

"You see the thing was he started coming around for sex and then he seemed to like *me*. I didn't want that. You have to keep them off in that way. Because it may just be a game for them. They're usually married. But I've got to keep going and I'm not giving up my time to anyone who doesn't give back solid—like gifts and things, I mean, or trips.

"But he kept coming back so often, and he did all the things out of bed which were really great. That made me fall in love, you know? He taught me things, and showed me things, and took me places I never had been to, and made me laugh a lot. We went out ordinary, which was the nicest. To the pub, or for a drive on a Sunday afternoon, or to visit my stepdad.

"He never minded me having other boyfriends, but after a while I didn't want them. If he didn't come around, then I stayed home alone, or went out with a girlfriend.

"Sometimes he even took me home, and his wife was very nice to me. She didn't know, of course. But he likes company and has a lot around him all the time, and I was just a girl around."

"Didn't she ever ask any questions about you?"

"No."

"Penny, perhaps she knew? Do you think so?"

"Oh, no. She was much too nice to me."

(I swear she knew. Tolerance has long limits, when you have a shrewd idea of the terms of your bargain.)

"Anyway," continued Penny, "the next thing, I stopped stripping."

"He asked you to?"

"Well, he didn't mind the *stripping*, really, but it was sometimes very inconvenient. Because he couldn't take me out until after the show each night, and he got bored with sitting through it first!"

She grinned, gleam-vulpine suddenly. "I don't blame him. There's a limit to how much of that stuff you can watch, and he seemed to be able to take a lot of it. But it was too much in the end.

"So he set me up in a glove-and-hat shop."

I fell about, laughing, "You're *joking*. A milliner's shop. Oh, my god."

She waited, serious and slightly irritated, for my guffaws to stop.

"What's so funny about that? It was a boutique really. It cost a lot of money."

She didn't get it, and I wasn't about to tell her. Tell her what? That for several generations gents have been doing some equivalent of setting up dancers, strippers, pretty-ones in milliner shops? Make her story part of the miniature meccano set?

*But a whole swarm of thoughts buzzed into mind, busy, flying everywhere. I had been read-*

*ing earlier that day about insects, flies in particular, and been intrigued by the fact that a species of balloon-fly catches its prey by spinning strands of tiny bubbles to form a spherical balloon, in which the prey gets embedded. In mating the balloon is transferred to the female, who makes no attempt to eat it, but just shifts it about from leg to leg while they copulate. Other males just carried small insects they'd captured, and when a female approached she would be attracted to the male holding the morsel and permit him to copulate with her for as long as the morsel lasts.*

*Into my mind swarmed the image of generations of human buzzers, our society's conspicuous successes, male-flies, bar-flies, super-flies, offering their prey to females, gift-wrapped, as lubrication for the mating, not as an answer to genuine need for food. I saw them wrapping up women, generation by generation, in little milliners' shops—for after all, there are only a limited number of means to an End.*

While Penny talked, her memory tumbling the words, her voice coming sweeter, more treble, as the memories grew troubled, I saw a man hitting the crucial two-third mark through his life, capable, brilliant I think, bored at home and anxious to grab backward, lifeward, youthward, sexward, meeting the little stripper, intrigued by the gaminess and pale tough independence, and setting her up in the milliner's shop.

Marrying her?

Possibly, if he was in the sphere of life where it would not produce so many practical difficulties that it was simpler to stay where he was.

It was the Same Old Story. Formula stuff. Except that while it *was* the same old story, I had to force myself to remember that it also wasn't: I'd been through enough of the ritual dance-dramas to understand this. For each time, as the flies swarm and the females buzz and the ancient imprinted moves are made, each pair thinking it different, each pair are both imitating the movements and mistakes of a myriad others, and are also, uniquely, themselves.

They *are* different. They are two particular people. Their *behavior* is another matter: insofar as they are animated by their behavior, they are automaton and pointless, ripe for the rubbish heap; gravely mistaken if they think that the well-reamed channels, grooved by generations, into which they fall, have special distinction, because it is *they* who have so fallen. The channels have no distinction; no interest. But the *people* do. *Penny* was a person, Simon a person. Potentially at any rate. And so was I, potentially. We not-people do well to remember that each mirrors the other.

*And so as I fell about laughing, it was for me too; for all of us caught, one way or another (till we could pick ourselves up and test the ground at our feet and start making for the exit door), in the spiderweb, the flytrap, spun by the Unspeakable Others: tangled nonsensical, witless, ancient-spun balloons into which we had tumbled; thinking ourselves actors and authors; but in fact we ourselves the prey in the balloon; and while we mated and hungered and thought ourselves re-*

*markably interesting, still only the prey in the balloon, rolled between the legs of the demons and phantoms, rolled frantically across empty shafts of Space. Wasted seed, adulterated impulse, and prostituted hope; misdirected love making the universe turbulent, rolling the demented prey inside the balloon until it pops, and we tumble, dollwise, to the ground, exhausted, convinced we have just had a Great Time in Bed.*

# Chapter 14

"What happened then, Penny. Did you really want a shop?"

And what would happen? Would they find their own way home? Would he wake her up, leave wife, rescue her from hats? Would they live happily ever after? Would the penis, mightier than the sword, smash the cobwebs?

I felt worse about her than about myself.

Penny wasn't very efficient in the shop. Simon, a financial wizard, found himself helping her more and more frequently in very many ways; more than he'd bargained for I suspected, but he couldn't bear to watch his money slip down the drain. Investments had to be good ones. So he became more than the man who kept her and paid high for the privilege, more than a business and sex partner even. He became what she had never had: her focus: her fixed fertile point: her father and friend.

*I remember picking up a tatty, secondhand paperback written by a girl who had been a Playmate. Her sexual using, at the hands of well-heeled, glamorous and respected members of the male profession, with whom, nominally, she was considered to be having and giving a "good time," was marked by selfishness, narcissism (Jeffrey-style), and a level of human perception probably, by that time, so low-grade as to be ineducable. After she had played their game she fell for a dope-pusher, a criminal subsequently in prison, who with her was open, honest, and appalled at the sexual barbarism to which she had been a prey. Human to human he educated her sexually, produced her first orgasms out of her, taught her a rudimentary human response. This, obviously, was where his "clear light" still burned. In that area, he was capable, truly knowledgeable, not as a sexual virtuoso who orchestrated the events which would somehow result in the extrusion of orgasm from her, but as an ordinary chap who knew about women. That was something he could do. That being so, he axiomatically could not do anything else with her.*

*You do what you can.*

Simon could do a lot for Penny, and so, in his company, a similar capacity became available to *her.* Slowly she opened up. The cage of her life grew larger and she had more variety. It even became one in which there were windows, with a view outside; and a place, though not yet quite visible, where a door might be. Like a blind person learning to see. . . .

But what Simon could *not do* he could not change—and his sexual behavior was apparently a buffered, segmented fragment of activity in which people switched off and the fucker and fucked took over. He had the use of his heart and his mind and his genitals, and he was a man whose tolerance of tedium in all three was low. Bed was where you fucked. No love there. Bed was genitals. Bed was physical tension strung by art and design to its limits.

Penny and I had, in fact, opposed difficulties. I was easy and familiar in my personhood, and unhappy because none could recognize both that *and* the female in me. Penny was recognized as a feminine all right, but had difficulties in being seen as a person. By treating her as Person, as well as and in addition to Bed Object, however, Simon began to turn Penny into someone who began to think about herself; who dawningly felt that perhaps with the security of his interest and attention, his physical presence, his cash, and his bed-satisfaction, she might begin to unwrap the old, painful places. She began to depend on him.

Her remoteness, her icy defense which made men want to melt or fire her, began, in Simon's gaze and energy, to melt and fire—and Simon found his pretty little girl friend beginning to stir into life.

At first it gratified him. Early on, it was neither raw nor noisy: just a touching testament to his enlivening affections. And his structure was safe. His wife was Person; explored Companion; boring in bed. Penny was Goddess Girl, with an edge of Personality beginning to show, which was consumingly attractive, like a smudge of dirt on an impeccable beauty. She was his goddess, sex maiden, and newling, unshaped girl-creature.

But he underestimated her powerful energies. Penny began really to wake. And as she behaved in the way that waking people do, so he behaved toward her in the way that he was used to treating people with minds of their own; without thought for their weakness, with impatience if they bothered him, with a lacerating tongue if they disturbed him.

Penny was turning into Wife: from Goddess to Slut.

And when Simon had transformed her totally from the one into the other, then he left her.

## Chapter 15

The longer I drifted in the fog, the more difficult and unpleasant even ordinary, simple things became, made heavy by the sediment of misdirected experience, mistake and muddle. I forgot even what little I had natively known, so that I became less wise at thirty than at twenty, less knowing, less perceptive. I had a nose like a hawk for freaks, heads, kinks, and twisters, no matter how decent or straight they looked; I could sniff out a personality-wobble or a security-shake like a truffle hound.

But good, plain, simple things escaped me, most of the time.

My light-beads were deep in the mire again, limed over by the guano of the world. Ordinary responses, which I had counted upon, even these became difficult to execute, and an achievement when managed: the triumph of a spastic managing to put one foot in front of another. I was like a creature photographed in slow motion, struggling through a barrier of dense air; a resistance of air. Progress was out of the question. I was in triumph when I heaved to, so to speak; I was in familiar day-to-day state when I drifted backward.

One could always spot newcomers to Fog. Those who drifted in still animated; able, through their energies, to take advantage of the mindless, bereft creatures we had become; laughing and exploiting the doped, drugged stupidity of those they came in touch with.

There was a whole wave-wash of acrobatic black men, one year, new to England, with the energy of sun and green still in their bones and blood, unlike the dank moss growing in ours. Once I went to a party where they were operating—in "liberal" circles, that word which was used to indicate the particular affliction of mildness and appeasement of those who gravitate to and profess these principles: "We must be decent, everyone must think us nice, violence is Frightful. Good chaps we." (For how dreadful if we were not.)

I watched one dapper, cocky black man ask the beautiful draped females, one after another, to dance. They would be tantalized, won by his steady beat of male energy. He would take them, hold them close, grind his knee instantly into their crotch and when they tensed and recoiled ask, hurt: "What's wrong? You don't like black men?" Alarmed at the thought of such a torn slip actually showing, the girls would protest too much that

black was beautiful and cuddle close. He went
out of his mind with manic glee with the pickings
of that night.

But I saw him five years later, and he, too, was
slowed and fumbling, puzzled at what had happened to him; at how the moss-muddle and dark
had overgrown and tied the quickness of his mental movements, the monkey agility of his life-de-
light.

There was another black man, too, happy and
hopping when he arrived, whom I met again in
the depths of the darkness. One small and dreadful aspect of his nature had been fed in the fog,
until what might have died in a healthier environment from lack of nourishment and breathable
atmosphere flourished and took control of his
whole sexual nature. I went to a couple of parties
and watched him, approaching woman after
woman, until he found her. His gambit was always the same. Dance. His body warming hers.
And then: "I want to go to bed with you tonight."
Murmured, male-strong; even male-tender; the
dominant male of the romances. If she was the
one who said yes, then he would dance on, binding her close in the silky threads of nerve-end-
ings in a mesmeric envelope of frisson and chill,
until she was swaddled, and drawn tight in his
quiver. Then he would really draw his bow. He
would say, she so close and throbbing that already
she was victim: "And will you let me hurt you?"
Having drawn her complicity, or shortly after
that, I would see them leave together: he grim,
satisfied with the execution to come; she trem-

bling, and over her the aura of delicious fright.

I suppose it was hell, really. The torments of the failed; and while failing, damned. But to those of us who were inmates, it didn't feel like hell. We weren't important enough for that. We were lost souls who thought we were safe because we had never *begun* the losing journey; ahead, so we thought, there was still promise—Hell was somewhere else, for people of consequence, in another time, or another place, a Renaissance ornament, a churchy bogeyhouse. That is one of the efficient tricks of Hell; its window-dressing is so accomplished that you mistake the wares until you have sampled and sunk.

Indeed, many of my associates were touted by the respectable world and word-of-mouth fashion as desirable beings, on the strength of one decorative aspect of their fractured lives. A simple countryman would never have mistaken them. But 'civilized' opinion could be duped.

At this time which was, chronologically, shortly after Penny had broken down completely, as they say (meaning only that Simon's heat had melted the glue in her carefully papered personality), and she was under specialist care, as they say, which is a hoot; I too found myself swept by fog-swirl into flurries of doctors, therapists, scientists.

In some sort of sympathy for Penny, who had been such a close friend, I found myself attracted to them. For Penny reflected my own chaos back at me.

I also found myself questioning the components of my mind and nature more closely than it had occurred to me to attempt before.

My nerve was beginning to go.

The girl who laid down the law with such competent ferocity about the granite goddesses, the weirdos, the frozen English, began to wonder whether there wasn't something odd about her too.

For I was becoming someone I would have hated to meet, had I been told about her five years before. Emotionally numb, life-and-passion numb, moving in a nimbus of free-floating anxiety, and stubbornly promiscuous—ensuring that through the sheer weight of numbers there would be some bargains among the duds.

And often, if I avoided the most savage of the derelicts, I was thoroughly physically satisfied by strangers if they, as I, were also opting for one or two nights' straight physical pleasure, without overtones or extras.

Two nights was about as much as I could manage without beginning to see the lineaments of the *person;* becoming, thereby, in some way involved with them. Then the whole arrangement would get confused, I would want to give, or get, or exchange with them. And so I ruthlessly set the deadlines.

The satisfactions during this period came least often from the nominally respectable members of the society. They had no notion of how to keep it clean, and tended to treat women like whores, or phantoms of their own devising. They were no respecters of privacy; would think that a tumble in bed entitled them to prowl all over my mental house. Or would think the other side of that same coin—that I was "dirt." Their idea of a woman was one crude notion which somehow covered all comers—tits, cunt, arse, and a pretty face, perhaps.

If, by accident, some individual characteristic penetrated through to them, the unexpected shock was enough to make them think they were in love.

I heard many sorrows.

Most were the result of confusing the idea for the reality.

There was the showbiz promoter whom I comforted in bed one night. He had just lost his fortune.

His fortune was a young girl he was going to turn into a sex-symbol superstar. He'd had her nicely on the way. A dishy child. She could have had it made. Him too.

"Silly cow," he said, "I had to pack it in with her."

"Why?"

"I told her she had to get to bed early each night and spend her days in the beauty shop and all that crap, and not drink, which was bad for her skin, and not go with men. And what happens? She's larking about at parties till three in the morning, fucking around with all and sundry, drinking champagne on the river at dawn, living it up."

He got a bit irritated when I let out a bellow of laughter.

"Oh Christ," he said, "I've got another right one

in my bed. What's so funny?"

I'd just learned something. That was what made
me bellow. Sex symbols are phantoms.

They're not expected to *do* it.

I learned, finally, how to say no firmly. A trendy,
florid drunk took me home from a party, I accept-
ing the lift after making it clear he couldn't spend
the night, long before he asked. "OK," he said,
not believing me. "OK."

When we got to my place he lunged. I was un-
shakable. I'd warned him.

So he used my phone, rang his boyfriend, and
unembarrassedly pleaded with him to let him
come up there.

"I don't want to be alone," he said pathetically.

Any bed is warm.

In all my promiscuity I found scientists to be
best. Not the headmen, who, as shall become
clear, were beastly. But the open-minded experi-
mentalists, practical and pragmatic; the men who
computed what would happen with different
combinations of variables and tried; who were
used to experiments failing as no great tragedy
and simply tried again in a slightly different way;
who were trained to read responses; and trained
also to keep their own emotions outside their experiments. Poets, psychologists, philosophers (all
the heads, in fact), are used to mixing themselves
deeply into the crucible of their molten life-mate-
rials, and tend to keep their frontal lobes func-
tioning while losing their heads.

But Scientists can honor their raw materials

while keeping a proper distance; can walk away from an experiment in order to go home for dinner, and then come back later with undiminished readiness to devote energy toward the project. A good scientist, and I speak from delightful experience, has the edge on a good poet, who tends to live in a low-lying cloud of ego and melodrama and emotion, in spite of the propaganda and folklore which has the poet sighing and anguishing at each whim of the mistress he loves. For the poet gets so wrapped, rapt, that he is hand-and-mind tied.

But the scientist—ah, the scientist—if he does his daily job with any flair, has a constitution which combines the poet's prodigious imagination with his own discipline's pragmatism.

As in the lab, so in bed, so to speak. And I speak so from experience. If my dear Jonathan, who was a Nobel Prize-Winner, approached his work as he approached me, then no wonder he walked off with that accolade. In bed he was experimental, imaginative, inventive, ingenious, generous, and funny. What was more, he had a basic and thoroughgoing knowledge of anatomy, and the body's potential responses.

Between us, Jonathan and I must surely have found out every surface understanding of the body's circuitry and responses. We spent together long days and nights of careful building energy, of laughter, and seriousness, and affection, and renewal. Sometimes I thought I would die if he pushed me further. But I would laugh, and thrill, and stay alive.

Always, we kept our pleasures and our emotions nailed firmly into our bodies' needs.

Jonathan was one of my threads of Accidentals —that term used in music to denote that something happens, out of the running and predetermined course of things, at *that moment;* not elsewhere. It was my many Accidentals who saved my life during the long fog. People, journeying themselves, with whom I could light a campfire and warm myself for the voyaging ahead. Ships that *pass*, as they say; not ships that crash.

There were no prejudices or inhibitions between us. Once, when I suspected that the particular Accidental named Jonathan may have produced an Accident who in nine months would also need a name, Jonathan waited until my womb was open from orgasm, and then put the hand that had been holding me in love-making one moment earlier right into my depths, deftly and clinically, to examine the possibilities.

It would have sent Jason screaming with terror.

But it was cleaner and more open (as well as being crucial) than something which happened to a young friend of mine that very same week. (Do friends' crises come together, the way it has now been established that the menstrual periods of women who associate together tend to do?) Anyway, young and pretty Wendy went to a middle-aged doctor, short-portly in build, as the tailors would say, and he—once he had impressed his high seriousness on her—spun her a line about the research he was doing and how all his female patients were expected to take part in this. He laid her on his narrow examination bed, stood over her, and then—with her *paying* for this consultation—made her masturbate to orgasm with a vibrator.

The poor addled girl thought it was compulsory.

## Chapter 16

Although the good scientists can't be bettered, there is this danger with technical men, that they will blind their victims with their science, if they can. Of them all, I think that the psychologists are among the worst, the most dangerous beasts of the dark. The ugly things they did to Penny have no place in this story.

In the name of healing, they experimented with the kind of cure which exactly matched their *own* disease; not hers.

The psychologists I fell among were safer, because I only knew them socially—which often didn't stop them wielding their expertise over the coffee cups, and using their clinical dogmas as pricks to crack one's guard and get one into bed. All of them professed an interest in things of the mind, but they usually preferred that mind to belong to someone else. I am not too sure whether I fell in with them, or whether they tripped me up and then caught me. Either way, and I suspect it was the usual two-way-mirror effect, I became their fond object for study and anatomy and—if they had wreaked their will—vivisection.

These psychologists, nature's little helpers, who are interested in disease at its deepest and most "interesting", were the omnipresent tyrants of the fog. The first one I ever met, shortly after arriving in England, was a Freudian, now considered an outdated mode of inspecting and labeling, but then quite the rage.

He was all steam, and no engine.

He tried, timidly, to take me to bed, projecting the impression that he didn't have to do much more than announce his wish, and my reaction—if it were anything less than straight compliance —was going to be interesting, in that it would reveal, psychologically speaking, my complexes and lacks.

He did not have the strength to ask me as himself, so to speak, but masqueraded as this Freudian Dignitary, who had, somehow, a *droit de seigneur* over my sexual behavior. When I refused, laughing actually, because he really didn't seem either serious or needy, he said, pouty and pigeon-mouthed like a little boy justifying losing the game, that I had no sense of my own femininity.

My jaw dropped. What did he mean? I had never heard about such things before. I was still new, and green—in more senses than one; and in the best sense. Flabbergasted, I asked him to explain himself. I didn't think he was much of a man, for that matter, but after my experience with Jason, I would never have unmanned him by telling him so. I think he was probably relying on some sort of immunity of this kind.

We were in a restaurant. He looked across, and pointed out a painted, blousy, ring-weighted, flaccid creature, with skin like old marshmallow, popping young and tender morsels of food fatly and delicately in her gobbler. Female all right. I grant you that. Sow-female; easy to be that if you could bear to let yourself go in that direction.

And our Expert of the Mind, if he was to be believed, was for some reason, most probably to anneal his own pains, trying to feed me the notion, if I would swallow and stomach it, that taffeta-porkey across the room, wearing her jewels like sweat, cuddling with her swinish paramour, was in some way morally "better" than I: someone worth emulating.

He was dead serious. I have met many like him since, duped to the eyeballs with their own propaganda, and yet taking professional responsibility for the mental health of others. He was incapable of conceiving, I think, that femininity might be other than what he had been told by his Master, frigid, rigid, puritanical Mr. Freud; incapable of wondering if there was more to my "femininity" than what was visible; or of speculating that there might be more to the person sitting opposite than a walking textbook he had read many times before. I was thankful that only the tip of my iceberg, so to speak, was visible—and disguised from him even so.

For old dingly-dox, the analyst, would have fouled each bit he got hold of, and one could only bless the arrangements that insured that he was sufficiently obtuse not to be aware of the fact that there were goodies, so to speak, close at hand but beyond his grasp.

What I discovered about the psychological gentlemen is that, one and all, they turned out to be suffering themselves from the very diseases that interested them most. Thus, once again, the mirror. We see ourselves in others.

*And so in this memoir, in writing the story of the failings of all these others, I am writing the accurate story of my own failure. If you are in a situation, you cannot be immune from it. Servant and master, hunter and hunted; turn and turnabout; the qualities are in the enveloping air.*

Dingly-dox was piglike himself. He would have rutted well with pork-and-beans lady in the restaurant. He was also, like the rest of his kind, such unfair game that one had to leave him to his illusions. Freudians are the easiest in the world to unman and unmask, simply by altering the boundary lines of their game.

But these other psychologists, the ones who nearly did me in, were somewhat more Modern. Wielding the latest ideas, they were more difficult to fight off: for a phase, I, as many others, was dazzled by the blinding newness of their slogans.

They decided I was an interesting and worthwhile lay study: someone threshing wildly, by now, in the toils of escaping hope and leaking skill but never quite going under; reflecting back at them aspects of themselves they were confounded

by but had under tight rein; keeping these sup-
purating wounds dry under their hats, their skins,
their noses.

But I, flailing wilder, was beginning to hit bottom, unable to hold body, as well as mind, together; so turbulent were my thoughts that physically
I was buffeted and blundering; as blundering
stoned as any have been on drugs.

I could not stabilize or center; my internal gyro-
scope had lost its steadying spin. I was ungov-
erned.

And I was a spectacle: an interesting specimen
for many more than the psychologists. Some, the
fixed and respectable, confined themselves to es-
say writing, with me as the subject, at the dinner
parties of others. Congratulating themselves on
their upright posture, they observed and patro-
nized me. I was inferior, good for conversation
and gossip, a quick slap on the rump or contemp-
tuous fondling, or simply for cold put-downs in
the office or at the bar. Listing, drowning, falling
off my stool: they would observe, shuddering, my
lack of sense, as though it were a personal affront
to good taste, and walk away.

There were others, whom in the jargon one
would call "problem oriented," who would have
liked to huddle with me and celebrate our mutual
difficulties, making the failure to make sense in
the maze the lynch-pin of a new in-group cult:
the more elaborate and ornamental the failure, the
more interesting the devotee.

I could have been their priestess. But I am not
a joiner of anything. Never have been.

Never, yet, had I met one who had come through. As an article of faith, I believed it possible. Whether I had encountered one I did not know. There was too much blood before my eyes for me to have seen or registered. Perhaps someone was there, waiting quietly around a corner, steering clear because there was nothing, yet, to be done. Although invisible, seemingly nonexistent, I was later to learn that people of this kind existed, and would later act, by their very existence, as witnesses to another possibility; providing by example—not by proximity, sermon, or even interaction—a strength on which I could draw. But not yet. Not yet.

*Not yet, because the mirror could not yet show them. This business of attraction is very exact. What is in your mind can be found in the other. One has heard it on all sides. Fix your mind on something, and it will come your way. It can hardly not. Because we mirror and match. Sex in my mind finds the sex in yours. If it is absent there, you will not see it in me. Hope in your mind will mirror the hope in mine, and where they meet and mirror the roadway can open further—down your mind or mine is hardly material.*

And although I was sinking fast, I could not find those able to help because, glutton for punishment, I was not yet finally sunk. Had not yet hit, if not bottom, at least the farthest point down that I was prepared to go before I'd had enough. Something in me, the curious ape in me, the savage in me, could not pull back before coming almost to the edge of the precipice and seeing the drop. Then I would turn and charge in the other direction. Only then, seeing the view to the pit, would I have had enough; would my thoughts no longer be to find answers in terms of my particular version of the goddess, the earth mother, the sex kitten, the good fuck, the happy home; would I drop all expectation, anticipation, supposition, and art-worked, poker-worked anticipation.

So that, as there is in front of the air pilot's nose in his plane, or the surfer on his board, there is clear air once more in front, where the step is to be taken. When one thinks one knows what form the improvement should take, one can miss the real thing when it stares one in the face. My need was soon to be rid of the dreadful, no matter what the cost, unknowing of what was to come.

But I *still* had a strong notion of what the improvements should look like, and as my desperation and frenzy grew, so it was matched in what I found in others. I began riding with the most dangerous kind of poseurs, charlatans, and psychological quacks—the power merchants.

But, snob till the last, I rode only with the best. I could spot inferior brands easily: like the man I once saw in Hyde Park, preaching meditation and bliss in the ranting, frothing, hectoring, hoarse tones of the raving fanatic, so these too offered their specifics and panaceas and elixirs, so-called, with a fascist screech: "goddam let me help you—or else." These were ludicrous. By which I mean, these, at least, could not snare me.

But my blind spot had remained unchanged. Blind to start with, how to learn to see in the dark, while flailing to keep my balance, shit flying in front of my eyes.

Thus the blind spot still ... the headiness I felt for the quality of Certainty, however expressed; unchanged, this faltering confusion and hunger since childhood. And though I was better at spotting the phonies, if one came along who knew something I didn't, once again I fell.

The psychologists, eponymous, self-styled, watched, observed, dissected, and finally decided that I was juicy enough to operate on. There were three of them: painter, shopkeeper, and schoolteacher; otherwise husband, divorcee, and bachelor; otherwise he-man, homo, and demi-virgin; otherwise fool, fool and fool. Soon they had to add a fourth fool to their shop sign.

For a brief while, I joined the firm.

I think they saw me as some kind of belly-dancing laboratory rat, who could be trained to tricks, be pushed to its behavioral limits, and then cut up for the secrets it could yield.

Or perhaps as some flavor-packed giant egg, roc or auk or ostrich even, which they could crack to make an omelette.

And yet ... I owe them some gratitude. As events fell out, in my blind fury at the spectacular con job they managed, I was shocked, for a moment, into clear air—saw where the bolt hole was, the eye of the fog where stood the exit hatch, and ran.

They, of course, wrote me off as a weakling failure, unable to stay their course.

Indeed I was. I bolted with a little lit match between my ratty, eggy paws, dragging my wounds behind me.

I rebounded onto these three after the collapse of what was virtually a second, brief marriage, to one of my scientists.

# Chapter 17

I met Alain, microbiologist and randy gourmet, when I had the moist sparkle of success clinging to me, for I'd just published a posh vol. of glossy photographs of the celebrated and the up-and-comers of the decade, with a quaint and personal text. It was quite voguey for a month or two.

In the pecking order of fog, in fact, I was doing fine. Dying though I might have been, it was disguised to others by the fact that I had put down some sooty roots, goods-wise; had a pretty flat, nice knick-knacks; stylish clothes; and had this highly desirable Alain, with whom I resorted now, for three years, five days a week, taking my rest and adventure on the other two while Alain returned to wife and kids.

I really like Alain. He tempted me to set up house in the fog, if I could have one such as he as my partner. In fact, when from time to time our passions rose high, I nearly forgot my search for my necklace of light-beads, and considered settling down with Alain—given that I could have prised him from his family.

In fog's terms we were remarkably well matched: sexually inventive and receptive, with our sex life renewing surprisingly often and easily; changing, almost with the seasons, into new and heightened styles of pleasure. And along carefully laid down and tested paths we stimulated each other mentally.

But I never mentioned my bafflement and bother with fog, my own and other people's, because he didn't seem to notice that we were living in it.

That apart, we were great together. The fact that we were both somewhat on the make, socially, professionally, produced nothing but mutual respect. We were like petty criminals in a partnership based on the lowdown we had on each other. From time to time we nearly forgot ourselves and tried to sneak in a quick theft at home, to keep our hand in; and then remembered, with good humor, that there was honor among thieves. And anyway it wouldn't work.

One thing I relished about Alain, who had central European blood, was that he absolutely adored women. There had been many in his life. He disarmed me utterly when we met, after the first time we had made love, when he looked at me steadily and said, "I want to know everything about you."

Wow.

For years I'd been looking for someone to tell!

Until its break-up, my three years with Alain

don't really have a place in this memoir, which is, after all, an anatomy of what goes wrong. The only relevant information, therefore, is that in the end, I became attuned to Alain to such an extent that I forgot about myself and my own needs.

Not unselfishly. It was laziness, really. Alain was there. It was comfortable. The relationship explored everything except the thorny items, such as our deepest feelings and our mutual ambiguities—and even these, at first, *seemed* to be exercised. In retrospect I think we both saw that we were only repeating sentiments we had both expressed, piecemeal, elsewhere; reporting back from other times.

And finally, he was not committed to me. Although I think he might have felt more deeply about me than I about him, *his* life had a structure and a funkhole, namely his other wife and family; while mine, apart from weekends, came to be filled by Alain.

But the basic difficulty was unbreachable. Alain was habituated to fog; adapted for bad air. The idea that clear air might exist somewhere, perhaps even close, seemed to him, as an automatic reaction, implausible and soft-headed; and seemed, when I pushed him to considering it more deliberately, an obscene personal insult, evoking in him raging anger, blinding rudeness, and finally deep disquiet.

Yet he was softer headed than I. In everything but his laboratory work he was poetic and irrational; sentimental almost; certainly primitive in his thinking. And what for him represented a re-

spectable total life's achievement—his own position, hierarchy-wise, in the foglands—was for me,
in my terms, only partial; there still existed an im-
measurable loss and an incompleteness.

Unconsciously, he manipulated our parting. Scientist Alain indulged in a piece of sympathetic
magic calculated to bring ruin. He didn't intend
it that way: in fact he initiated his action as a
ritual of forestalling, propitiating magic. Unfortunately, he reckoned without me. I took him
literally, not seeking the nervousness under his
comments, and eagerly cooperated in making the
dreaded thing happen, turning what he was trying to repel into a magic to attract.

Like this. He had often told me stories about
Arthur, the most fascinating sexual monster in the
high-bohemia we lived on the fringe of. Alain, as
a scientist, was fascinated, as many of his kind
are, by music. He had spent a brightly remembered year in his teens traveling with a pop
group, and had become, during that time, an ad-
mirer of Arthur's talents for getting girls. No
slouch himself in this respect, he still made obeisance to his master, or at least, would learn from
anyone. And somehow this respect had continued,
unexorcised, into Alain's thirties when Alain was
somewhat tempered and Arthur was somewhat
gross.

One day I met Monster, as I now thought of
Arthur, and idly mentioned this. All Alain's considerable magical talents—which he would have
denied he had, but how did he think he'd made
his scientific discoveries?—heaved themselves into motion. He activated the formulae: to describe

is to pin down; to picture is to render powerless; to say is to stop. He talked about Monster day after day, reminiscing fondly, marveling drunkenly, teasing my imagination with his speculations about what it was about Monster that got him all the girls.

He never realized that it was the sort of cooperation he had from the dazzled Alains. It took a month, and I'm surprised it took that long. Within four weeks Alain had sold me on the idea that my life would forever have missing some vital piece of sexual information if I didn't put in a little time between the sheets with this Rabelaisian being who had virgins for breakfast, orgies at noon, and unspeakabilities after his late night show.

Small wonder that one weekend, after Alain had left to see his wife, I packed my bags, and oozed off like some voracious, fluttery, cartoon character, avid and smirky, toward Monster and his Bed.

Thus the uses of propaganda.

I went to the bar where Monster, all teeth, red cheeks, jester nose and paunch (and in fact also well dressed and witty), was known to hang out come sundown, relaxing between snatches, so to speak. We greeted warmly, exchanged catchphrases while sniffing each other out, and then he said dinner? and I said yes, and he said with lots and lots of lovely wine? and I said oh yes, and he said and BED? and I said yes yes yes.

Comparatively speaking it was very nice. Had we teamed up for a couple of weeks, it could have become exceedingly nice, a pastime undertaken with initiative, variation, and a kind of small boy cuddly zest. It was odd that the most intriguing sexpot of those climes should seem more like a large teddy bear than anything else. The ambience was of kids in a street gang, having secrets. Fun. Almost like a more adult version of the "doctor" games I used to bribe my little friends to play with me.

After making love he left his hand between my legs for comfort, and amiably rambled on about the pleasures in his life, affectionately including me as one of them. I snuggled and slept, and then returned in kind. He was neither shocked nor fascinated. Just a tender roué; a good listener. All cuddles. No kinks.

In the morning I dressed, we said goodbye to each other with immense goodwill, knowing nothing else was required on either side, and I came home to Alain, composing in my head the sentences describing the interesting things that had happened to me. I really thought Alain had wanted to know, had been so ceaselessly curious about the Monster's talents, that my bringing him the information was a light-hearted act of generosity. Bringing home a present for one's dear one which one's dear one has hinted many times he would like. What a lovely surprise he would have!

Brightly, naively, I told him. Adding: "You know, I think it's just the build-up, that's all. The pop stuff, the music, his brilliance and all that. In bed he's jolly nice, quite ordinary, and not half as marvelous as you. And he's quite straight, you know. There's nothing mysterious. . . ."

Alain hit me. He'd been chewing his lip while

I rattled on, clenching and unclenching his fists.

Then he bit down on his teeth and grabbed my shoulders and shook me, and threw me through the door.

I still didn't quite register why he was angry. He couldn't be serious, could he?

"Are you cross?" I gasped unnecessarily, as I limped back into the room. "You've no need to be. I didn't mean...."

"You deliberately went and slept with him!" Alain was talking toneless, breathing hard.

"Yes, of course. Weren't you keen to find out...?"

"You must be an imbecile."

"Well, I thought..."

"Did you bother to find out if his VD has cleared up? The dose he got from..." He mentioned a well-known nightclub singer.

How did *that* creep into the conversation? And why did Alain sound grimly satisfied, so maliciously pleased, about it?

I looked at him bleakly.

"I could kill you," said Alain, and hit me again.

The state of murderous high-tension lasted for a week. At one time Alain's complaint was: "How could you do this to me this week of all weeks, when I have an important conference coming up? I can't think straight!" which I thought was justifiable. Had I known the effect it would have on him, I certainly shouldn't have bothered.

And on another occasion it was a baffled wail, head down, bullwise thwarted: "How *could* you! And after I have been absolutely faithful to you, *always.*" It seemed to me that rankled almost

most. For the first time in his life he had, in his fashion, been faithful; and for the first time in his life, being faithful, he had been deceived.

I was numb. I really had done nothing consciously, logically, to hurt him, and I was waiting for him to realize that, so that we could return to normal. I couldn't quite understand why he'd taken it so hard, although when he told me exactly what it meant to him I was overwhelmingly remorseful and sobbed. I hung about, white-faced, waiting for a chance to make amends. He iced me for a week, then took me into bed once more, then packed and walked out.

I could hardly believe it. Tears, yes. Hurt, yes. But over for ever! Surely not. I didn't feel any different toward him. I'd spent three years with him as my chief thought of each day. I'd been happy in his company. I had grown rather in his shape. And he could uproot it so easily.

The terror was, that he uprooted it so abruptly that he pulled up half my roots with him as he walked away. So that I was left, alone, a phantom of myself, my psychological innards packed up tightly inside Alain's mind and body, and he moving around the world freely with them, and I a zombie back at the ranch.

# Chapter 18

Alain took his revenge. He installed a girl in the flat across the hall, and with her remained incarcerated for a week, while I was rolling, screaming, yelling on the floor of my flat, my vital parts still bedded somewhere inside Alain, who was passing it over to the faceless, nameless female he was poking, thereby punishing me and exorcising me.

I picked myself up and carried on, daytimes, but (outside from my work) lax and limp. This was the deepest hurt yet. How many more could I afford in my life? Certainly, there could be no more lighthearted flings in me; my lightness had been ploughed into the foreigner flesh in the bed across the hall. My surfaces now were eroded. There was no soil left for the growing of a shady, firmly rooted bower. There was nothing left of me at the easier reaches.

Those who could find me now would have to dig down to rocks. They would have to put their fingernails deep inside, and pull back the soft, secret membrane that covered my real depths. I was a wound, protected only by the final layer of my skin.

And Martin, the head psychologist, went to work on this pink, soft protection—avid for the dense goodies underneath.

*Fog is nowhere. But it is also a subculture; for all practical purposes, a closed system. Deep in its center, where it moves densest and quickest, in the spin of its vortex, there is its eye and exit; the chance to translate into life. But near that eye pandemonium rages, and few old lags venture there. It seems more tolerable in the surrounding wastes; there it kills more slowly, and existence, in its mugginess, seems almost "normal."*

*The norm merely requires that the paid-up members should say, convinced: "Fog is all . . . Fog is It," as Alain did, and "The rest is fantasy and dream." It requires, too, that the kingpins of the fog, those creatures who make it to the peaks of the smoky castles, should appear enviable to their fellows; should seem to them worth emulating; possessors of territory worth fighting for.*

*They must be convinced, in fact, that there is nowhere else to go.*

*In my stay in the fog I have watched the braver ones appear to contradict this. Some stagger toward the eye of the fog, groggy but determined, and are then bowled over by the turbulence there,*

*and tumble back, confessing: "It is as they say.
We are trapped. But I have been farther than any
man." And then they settle in, and cash in, and
make a fine living out of repeating, in one form
or another, their experience to others.*

*That, too.*

*The fact that there may be other, quite or-
dinary, chaps moving at will in and out of this
low-lying pall, stopping in now and then because
they need to be there, or need to travel through
it at that moment, never occurs to the denizens.
It is a thought normally screened out because of
the pain its brings.*

*And so my companions and I set up our blurred
hierarchies and pecking orders, and established
our rules, and invented punishments for disloyal-
ties. Those who came in and out from the fresher
air beyond failed to learn, at their cost, how to
travel the foglands incognito; how to look like all
us other kids who had turned the fog world into
play world; dirty world into escape world; booby
hatch into real world.*

I met Martin because, once again, I had to take
his picture. He had just written a black, sexy, psychological treatise which was aimed at flipping
the lids of all the disenchanted, young and old,
and his publisher was promoting this idea as if his
author had fashioned single-handed, the holy
grail. I honestly didn't think much of his book,
but flipped over Martin himself.

His was a lovely face to try and catch, because it varied so. The challenge was to find the

common elements in all his expressions and glances. He had hooded eyes, a brooding stare, sometimes a manic mad-eye wildness, at others a shrunk stoop, like an old child, small-shouldered and burdened. At times he seemed like an aging, snaky savant inside the skinny body of an adolescent. At others, when he had drunk too much, or drugged too long, he would seem like some kind of ancient god—a poor man's bacchus, or dionysius, or vulcan.

The fact that he purported to be an expert on women rendered me snake-fodder almost before we met. I was fascinated. When I went to his flat for our session he stood and stared at me on the threshold, before letting me in; a cool, sexy, insolent stare, daring me to look away, telling me I had failed some test if I did.

I held it longer than decency required, then dropped my eyes.

With satisfaction, he dourly asked me to come inside.

He bullied me in those first moments, and continued to do so during our association. I was sunk when I had not looked away fast, disinterested, dismissing. Before I broke, we saw something of each other's depths. I saw black maleness, malevolent almost, but of a strength and certainty that hooked me. And he? I never asked, but in many ways in the ensuing weeks he let me know it was untested femininity.

He was right, for the wrong reasons. Yet seeing something in another brings responsibility, I had always thought: not the license to fiddle, like a savage who may be able to read the time, but out of curiosity will break the delicate workings of the watch.

The session went badly, to begin with. I was too nervous and edgy; he was uncooperative. He was *above* this kind of thing, he indicated in his posture and behavior; only going through it because it was "done." But ultimately, we established a rapport as I spread my regard for his face across the air to his face itself, which relaxed under my interest in it, and must have sent the message to the rest of him. We became silently absorbed, both of us; working well together and talking in small phrases, I signaling my interests in between the commands for him to alter his postures.

I stayed on for lunch, and he continued to watch me, talking to me out of my depth, into my depths, never touching me, but fixing me with his mesmeric eyes, power-draining. My deference and attention was his staple fare, a necessary psychological fix. When he didn't get it he felt robbed, became violent. His due from all women.

By teatime his wife, Joy, and another couple who lived with them, had joined us. Martin had been questioning me closely about my life and hard times, and I was simultaneously telling and evading.

But by dinner time it was fixed, in principle, that I should join what was, in effect, their tiny commune. There was an American flute-player called Carl and his hysterical wife, Jean; and then there was Max, currently out of town, who had no mate. I would even up the numbers.

It didn't occur to me that if one cut through the philosophy behind it, unrepeatable here because of its high boredom coefficient, I was being invited in for two reasons only: Martin wanted a new victim, and he wanted to pimp for Max, the absent member.

It was merely a matter of giving up my worldly goods except the essentials (which for me was no hardship, though I failed to take a good look and notice that Martin held on to all of his) and move in with them. Work in the community was not exactly scorned, but really thought of as something for fools. As, however, I was the only one with a job which brought in any cash, I was told to keep working for the good of the group, while Martin pondered his latest prophetic visions and Carl twanged away dreamily composing visionary music.

It was understood that I would stop work when Martin's book paid off. Martin avoided ordinary work unless absolutely essential. He did not like to dirty his fingers by steeping himself in it; he was waiting for the book to scoop off, axiomatically, the first prize for being such a superior being.

Our lives had a very set pattern, which I thought of as boring until I was told I was being trivial. The women took turns at the cooking, and then, after the evening meal, we took long hauls on marijuana cigarettes and emptied our psyche-boxes and spread them around for everyone else to see. Practical criticism was the chief activity, and everyone—with the exception of me—was very good at it. I could never think of a thing to say. I couldn't understand any of their comments about me, and I couldn't summon the slightest insight about them. My true insight was so at variance with the general agreement that everyone was marvelous, that I jammed up.

I could not remember a thing about my own existence. When they asked me about my feelings about sex, about men, about my parents, about life, I would stammer dumbly. On the basis of what little they managed to discover, however, they made their decisions: I had never had a sexually releasing experience in my whole life, had never cringed and wept and sweated and screamed obscenities and broken under the male rod. No, I hadn't. Not like that. That was certainly true. So they brainwashed me, and I wonderingly took it.

And they indicated that when Max, the absent member, returned, all this might change, if I was a good girl.

The big sell, which I fell for, knowing what a mess I was in, was that we were all, in some way, Seriously Working on Ourselves, to be Better. A good intention, certainly; but angels are not made by manifestos, and we were the same shoddy lot we would have been without the declared intention.

And there was a hierarchy in all of this too, which was nice for the ones at the top end, and hell for the ones, namely hysterical Jean and me, at the bottom. The top people's problems were discussed in a kind of self-congratulatory way,

as interesting life-difficulties, which—to be fair—
they were doing their useless best to scrutinize.
But Jean's and mine were somehow less than
theirs; less interesting, less *worthy*, more easily
rectifiable if we would just follow their knowledgeable advice.

It was a convincing load of horseshit.

And it never occurred to me to leave. I was held
in thrall, as much as any titmouse by his granite
goddess.

During this period I was, for the first time in
years, quite chaste. No man I fancied matched up
with Martin's judgment of what a "real man"
was. I began to have delusions of grandeur, and
decided, myself, that John the Baptist wouldn't
quite do and it would have to be Jesus Christ
himself. For that was the level at which they
were pitching the mystical conjunction. Ordinary
workaday chaps were out, and I complied with
this because it stirred something in me as well.

For I *had* poured my search into sex; my life-
longing was for physical happiness, body and
mind, with another; thus I had been programmed,
and the punched card had not yet been dislodged.

These half-doctors both helped and hindered.
They confused me further by dwelling on and stir-
ring up material already so occluded and murky,
not knowing any proper way to help—if, indeed,
help was their motive. They did help me, I think
—but in a surprising way. They paid me a lot of
attention, the kind of regard I had missed out on
in my childhood.

Quite soon my chastity became a joke. Then it

was spoken of, one day, as frigidity, and over-
night that became my condition. The evening
conversations took their own momentum, and
projected onto me was the image of a woman
frightened of men, frigid, stumbling, helpless.
From the depths of my unsureness I could only
listen. They uttered words with such firmness, I
had little resource with which to make suitable
contradictory sounds.

Sometimes I had to work at night, and then the
assumptions about dear little Annie, as I was
fondly known, proceeded by leaps and bounds—
and I would sit wide-eyed and anxious, the next
night, to find out more of the horrors of what I
was like. I only half believed them, the rest being the same puzzling game one had to play to
"belong" as I had played, after all, since childhood. There was usually trouble after I'd missed a
night or two, because the group would have decided things about me which I had no notion of
and I'd be frantically guessing what the reason
might be for their further change of behavior.

"She can't relate," was one such fiat which was
handed around in my absence. And when I returned the next evening, I was confounded by
cryptic utterances and accusing statements, the
bases for which were obscure.

There was another difficulty: Martin's book. After a month of drummed-up agitation, it had
dropped into silence—some achievement for a
book on sex. He started recruiting his admirers,
his life-breath need, from those who had an almost pathological contempt for the media. For the

media hadn't even been shocked by it. It had
been ignored, which hurt him. At the same time I
was padding on fairly successfully, fairly unam-
bitiously now, at my profession. Martin would insult me and jeer at me for my lackeydom to the
media fools.

I fell for it, and dropped them. He hooted with
contempt at my contacts and my invitations, the
bubbling spread of my social life. It wasn't until
about three years later, when his book—which
had been merely premature for the fashion—enjoyed a belated success, that I realized the per-
formance had been based on jealousy. He adored
his success. Played being celebrated to the hilt.

I was dying, really, while thinking I was being
revitalized by this Serious, Sincere, Human Contact; this high-minded group working for Related-
ness; this disguise for a tribal cannibal rite.

And then Max came back from New Mexico.

He arrived in the morning, and they must have
buttonholed him, brainwashed him right away,
for that night they sicked him onto me. He was
fizzing with anticipation when I came home, and
for my part—having been fed many stories about
him—there was no question that he would break
my newly acquired chastity girdle.

He was a sweet guy; small, with new-washed
eyes; innocent, perceptive—and even more bug-
gered up than I. He was a decent fool, wander-
ing about the world having, I read in the instant
my eyes fell on him, even more trouble with it
than I. He was frail and frightened, but Martin
had fed him enough Dutch courage about my de-

ficiencies and his own capacity for undertaking my therapy, so that he marched into my bedroom that evening, pompously aware of his Great Task.

We chatted a bit, and I offered him a smoke.

"No, Annie," he said with great intensity. "We must do this thing clear-headed."

"How are we going to do it? I mean are we just going to peel our clothes off now, or are we going to slide into it pretending not to notice or what?" I asked, already bitchy, but scared and hopeful underneath.

It was as if I'd never been to bed with anyone before. I don't know what I expected.

He also seemed at a loss.

"Make me some coffee," he commanded, temporizing, playing manly.

Docile to the end, I complied. The mystification was complete. Experience and instinct both told me this was no sex-surgeon or psyche-mender.

Coffee was drunk in silence.

Then: "Come here," he said.

Came.

He undid the first two buttons of my shirt, then lost courage and said: "I'll take my clothes off now."

So nu? as we Jews say.

I stripped and got into the bed. And what I found in there with me was a young chicken, nesting in my feathers. He was still wet behind the ears, sexually speaking. I had to help, and show, and teach him. I couldn't find it in me to call his bluff; shake his pride. I responded weakly within

the tiny limits set by him, which was still over-
poweringly more than he appeared to be used to;
and I even tried, subtly, to extend those limits.

When the little deed was done, he lay, satisfied,
his arm around me, and lectured me. The moon
was shining full and clean; through the window
I watched the far stars; and he driveled on
about how the obscenity had now gone from my
face, how I had been honest for once in my life,
how easy and relaxed I was; how this was the
way I should be.

Bloody shit. I was looking good, I suppose, simply because I was wrapped in a softening sexual
aura; the heightened, velveting caul of sexual energy which wraps around one at such times;
nothing to do with what had happened between
us at all. So much for the Hard Sell, there between his legs, little and soft, which wouldn't
have mattered—the littleness thereof or even the
softness thereof—if his friends hadn't done such a
build-up job. That's all that built up.

They had forgotten they couldn't come in the
bedroom with him and shore up his cock—which
in their eyes was what mattered.

"You have to learn to be open, like this, always,
Annie," said Max out of the jauntiness of his
imagined achievement. I really don't know
how much sexual experience he'd had, but I doubt
whether it was very much. "You have to subject
yourself to the man, be generous. I can see into
you very clearly, you know. You must listen to
me."

I was still watching the moon.

"Shh. . . ." I quietened him. "Don't talk.

Sometimes it's better not to say anything."

I wanted to stop him before his pride became unbearable and my temper snapped.

"Yes," he said. "OK. You're right."

I think he imagined I was referring to the profundity of the moment.

He considered this an instant. Then added, kindly: "Even *you* can be right sometimes."

But he couldn't stop talking for long, and as he rambled on, patronizing me and lecturing me and hugging me with excitement, I hardened, and felt a kind of multidirectional contempt building inside me.

Then he slept, and I got out and sat on the edge of the bed, stony-faced, murderous. My flaming fury built and built as I sat there, until I was ready to kill him and eat him.

At dawn I was still there. I hadn't moved. Max woke, complacent. He seemed to have not the slightest desire to make love to me again, or even to touch me—though summer dawns are, to me, magically sexy times. He started talking almost at once. Now I knew what true love-making was, he said. He'd shown me.

He really believed it, the little sod.

I stared blindly out of the window, at the waking life of the gnats and midges, already wheeling, busy, in the sun.

How did I get here? I wondered.

I had the panicky feeling of being an alien. Lost. Off course.

Suddenly I was terrified.

Dimly I heard Max talking on; lecturing me

about the nature of life and my own psyche.

I made him a cup of coffee, and listened to him advising me to stick with him, for my redemption.

I am in midget land, I thought cloudily. I must get out.

But true to my training, I remained dumb.

## Chapter 19

Max never knew what had really happened. He reported back to the others, of course, who peered at me, and even, so help me, congratulated me at having "done it." I listened absently to the shit talked the next night, as the whole episode was rehashed and served up for conversation, and made my plans to leave.

I found a room, and announced that I needed a change of scene to think things out; that perhaps I wasn't quite ready for the wonderful emancipated life they were offering.

We lived through a day of tension-cracking silence before my departure. But I heard quite soon, from gossiping friends, any number of them, that they had found the suitable party-line on the matter. I wasn't strong enough to take the kind of honesty-demands of the relationship I had been offered; I was too romantic and idealistic about life; I was, finally, one of life's write-offs.

They said all this more in sorrow than in anger, as they adjusted to the fact that I had separated off from the buzzy hive.

They may have felt only sorrow simply because I had appropriated all the anger in that scene to myself.

For the first time in my life, I was seething with anger, simmering with fury. All the violence and indignation and outrage at the many cons dropped over my head over the years, from the steely butterfly nets of the delicate ones and the anaesthetist's masks of the despicable ones, all mounted into boiling rage, for Martin, for Max, for myself.

Willing victim, once again I had walked right into it. How long would it take before I learned?

Never again, I said to myself.

With interest, I noted now that Max had been right. There *was* obscenity in me. He had merely mistaken its source and course, as well as his own competence: he was a gnat who had seen what made the elephant stumble, and had then grown so inflated that he thought he could put the elephant aright.

I would wake in the middle of the night, now, gnashing my teeth and swearing and cursing. All my bitterest memories exploded around me; my deepest secrets were relived as if they had happened just the moment before. What had I done to myself? I would ask, panic-stricken, in the dark. First, by omission, not speaking up and standing on my rights to insist I saw what I saw? And later, by commission, when I became subject to others, saying to myself: if I do this often enough maybe I will get to feel like the rest of you.

Never again, I vowed to myself, muttering it over and over in the dark. Never again.

I have huge appetites.

I will associate with my own kind from now on.

Being of a practical nature, and recognizing the furnace poisoning me for want of an outlet, I sought reliable release in dancing. I found a jazz club in Blackland, that waste territory on the edges of Notting Hill, and in a smallish dirty basement, where no strong liquor was officially served, but where in spite of this many of the visitors were drunk or stoned, I danced, in the company of others who asked no questions and loved to move.

Most were black.

And there must have been something about me, now, some warning-off furious radiance, which made it impossible for anyone to come near me, to intrude, to want more from me than the moment of the dance. I went home, each night, alone, and dropped into sleep, as if slugged, as my head touched the pillow.

I danced, wild and vigorous; it was a private Orphic ceremonial.

Night after night, I blasted off some of the viciousness I felt and leaped, on physical search, toward these dear qualities, my own understandings, which I had jettisoned when I went into my pointless orbit and drift in the fog, in my teens, so many years before.

The movements of my dances would have been misinterpreted by polite society and frowned

on by opportunistic titmice. For they were exactly
what they looked like: the blatant signaling of
my rut-needing body, my tired but rechargeable
limbs. I danced out my bawdiness, rowdiness,
belly-laughter and obscenity; it was grinning, joking, death-dancing; whirling black-dancing.

*It was a yell through the ether for help; for res-
cue.*

At no time had I been one of those graceful sin-
uosities, prancing lightly near her partner with
the faint descriptions of earthiness and lust, but
never the wind and weight of those things themselves. But now, here, at the tiny, dingy club, I
transcended even my own kind of dance.

I finally let go.

Each night I would pace myself into the
rhythms of the music, sense my way inside them,
and then travel light-years from the dismal detri-
tus of my own and others' making; lifting my feet
higher and faster to leap clear from the mucky
rubble littering the earth's floor; shouting into
outer space for rescue and for help; laughing with
pure joy as I flew, grub into moth, groundling into bird, shedding my heaviness and tasting *myself,* and my coarse knowledge and then my fine
knowledge and then the knowledge which was
not only mine; flying, at last, with the rhythms of
drumbeat and heartbeat and starburst.

I didn't know how close I was to the eye of the
fog. I was frantic and burning. Mindless, I
thought I might be at the end of my world. Real

life, which I had longed for so many years before, seemed aeons away. I didn't even register that sometimes, when I danced, I would collect—yes— a bead of light.

I was too busy screaming for someone to save me before I burned to a crisp.

What I didn't realize was that the flames which I felt were consuming me were in fact probably saving me, cauterizing the worst of my miseries. There are many ways to die, and perhaps I might well have burned myself out then. But the noise I made probably helped, in a way I can't even now explain; helped, that is, in my rescue.

For at last I was loud enough for someone to hear my call.

And hear it, also, myself.

I was no longer drowning helplessly.

I was beached, and ablaze.

The escape hatch was almost within touching distance.

Then under my nose.

But I was holding my breath. Couldn't yet smell the clearer air.

And my eyes were tight shut.

So couldn't yet see it.

# Chapter 20

There was one more round of the circuit to travel —with the very people who idolized sex as deeply as I did myself, but who had institutionalized their idols.

I can hardly credit it. I walked into a sort of sex cult: a tangle of pagan worship, tantric yoga, and voodoo; tame stuff, really, because with one exception we were all decent Anglo-Saxon chaps, weren't we?

## STORY TIME

Dumas de los Angeles—yes, really!—gave me a heavy stare.

"You're one of us. You know that by now, don't you?"

Pregnant pause.

I wasn't too sure. Dumas, an urbane Trinidadian hustler, had been watching me at the dance club, had bought me coffees, and then invited me casually to dinner with two or three of his friends.

That was a few months back. They had steered the conversation round to the way people danced, and behaved, and made love, and *felt*—chiefly *felt* —about things. Passionately. I burst out with all the dogmas of their beliefs, only half believing them, but sensing this was what they wanted to hear. Sensing also that I was impressing the hell out of them, but not yet realizing that in my deranged state I was uttering all their aphorisms and catechisms.

"People in this town don't know how to let go!"

"Nobody takes risks with themselves and follows it through to the end. . . ."

"Emotionally, they're two-year-olds!"

"There's *much* more in life to be found. . . ."

"So much that is rich and wonderful is discounted . . . !"

OK. So I was an early flower-child.

They watched me dance, sometimes Dumas danced with me; but I wouldn't let him get too close. He had too much intensity; wanted to steer me; I, however, was flying solo and he had sense enough to leave me be. Until:

"You're one of us. You know that by now, don't you?"

Pregnant pause.

"Yes." Stared soberly back. "Yes, I am."

Am *what?*

Hang on. Temporize till you discover.

"Would you like to take it further?" asked Dumas. "We would like you to come to one of our meetings."

Panic.

Calmed.

"What form do they take?"

(Do I seem cool enough?)

"Oh come *on*. Like, you know, the way you dance? We go further. We worship, man."

Hope flared, a quicksilver snake.

Dumas knew things. His mother was an obiah-woman. I had watched his way with animals. He could mesmerize them. He once kept a dog in the cafe leaded to the floor. Still as stone. Did he perhaps *know* why I danced? What I sought?

"Yes. I'd like that."

(Would I?)

Dumas said nothing else. Drank his coffee in silence. When he left, I tackled his friend Ken. White friend. Too white. Long, skinny, promiscuous, too-white, too-tight Ken. The signals he sent out were all of an uptight, though he obviously believed his own propaganda—that he was God's swinging gift to woman.

What was Dumas talking about?

Ken was surprised. "Of course you know. You of all people."

"No. No I don't."

Ken scratched his head, and frowned. He took a deep breath. "What happens to you when you dance? How do you feel?"

"Free?"

"And when you make love?"

"That all depends, doesn't it?"

"When it's good, the best."

"Well . . . loose. Loosened. More me, if you know what I mean. But I can't hold it into every day."

"But that's *right!*" said Ken happily. "You do know."

"No, really not."

Ken's worry grew. "You're having me on."

For the life of me, I can't tell you how we got into the bind that followed. Ken had somehow convinced himself that I *knew* . . . whatever it was . . . and that I could only be some arch-secret inquisitor, high in the pecking order of whatever the cult was, putting him through some sort of test.

Looking over his shoulder nervously, he started: "There are techniques for taking it all further."

"Further? How further? Where?"

He jammed up. Peering round again, he coughed and then looked full at me, then dropped his eyes. *Blushed*, would you believe? "What do you want from me? You know all this."

"Not a blind thing, Ken."

"Yes you do."

The smell of his sweat was heavy and unpleasant. I could have made myself his lady-guru on the instant. He was ready to make obeisance. Perhaps it was because I was genuinely asking what he *really* knew—not the dogma to impress people, not the stage-setting and mystification and smoke screening—that he felt at a loss. He was wrapping himself up in knots; must have been confusing my fervid energy for some sort of conscious knowledge of how to use it.

It took ages to piece the bits he stammered out

together. But I gathered that a group of them met, fairly regularly, worked themselves up into ecstatic states, and then fucked.

It stirred something in me, to hear this. Some ancient haunting, unsurfaced thought. But I couldn't believe that Ken, who had been through this sort of ceremony, presumably, was any sort of exemplar of the liberation and knowledge he kept talking about. He didn't seem to know a thing.

But Dumas knew things.

Though even Dumas didn't exemplify what I wanted to know. If the hunger that drove me was to be satisfied in their cult, then why wasn't Dumas himself more interesting? Ken had hinted Dumas had all sorts of powers at his disposal. It was possible he did, for he had a compelling air. But fancy using it to score with girls, and hustle, and gain power over people, all of which Dumas did hypnotically well.

Boring.

Still . . . you never knew . . .

Until you have tried, it remains only your opinion. . . .

Maybe . . .

Thus I found myself in the woodland, on the Saturday night of a full moon. It was warm summer, with apple smoke soft in the air. And I embarrassed as hell, with my clothes off, and *icy* feet. There was Dumas, Ken, a tall tanned postman built like a king but with an absurdly servile personality, Ken's girl, who was like melting marshmallow, and Dumas's girl, stringy and boyish. There were a number of others, bright-eyed, well-mannered, playing it dead cool. I only half-glanced at them, eyes deliberately unfocused by the unexpected shock of naked parts around me.

That, I might add, wore off within minutes, but the tension and expectation of the whole occasion gripped me.

"I'll prepare Annie while you set up," said Dumas.

The women started unpacking an attaché case they had brought. One drew a circle with a sword, in what looked like a practice run.

"Shit," said another, rattling the contents of the case. "I've forgotten the wine."

"Could we use coke?"

"Have to."

One or two of them were jumping up and down, for warmth, like players before a game.

I was shivering. Dumas had drawn me under a tree, and was talking, intently and hypnotically, sending my mind to where hope and the stars lodged. But not like that, not like that. . . .

It was wrong, I could feel, because Dumas's motive was wrong.

He was doing it to rejoice in his own mesmeric powers. It was off-beam. Somewhere I sensed it and then put the thought aside.

"You have always known, Annie, haven't you . . . the elements and the energies of all life are in you . . . if you worship them they will give back life to you increased . . . tonight you will worship them with everything in you . . . you will worship them through the bodies of the other people here, but they are not *them*, as you know them every day, as you will not be you. . . ."

He talked, to my eyes, to my ears, to my skin, to my mind, caressing me as he spoke.

Somewhere behind me, a tape-recording of drumming had started, very softly.

Then he made me kneel, blindfolded me, spoke some magical-sounding words which seemed so idiotic they undid half the effect he'd had just before, and led me into the circle.

"Hold our hands and dance," he instructed. "Listen to the words of the ritual, and feel them in you."

A dodgy heart-shifting rhythm tapping softly from the mechanical box. Wet grass felt crisp and alive.

"Let what will happen happen," said Dumas. "Don't stop anything."

My hands were taken on both sides. Verses of worship to the Powers were spoken.

Dizzying.

Dance with us until you dance apart, I heard Dumas say.

Another voice intoned the verse. Lit crit warred with instincts that wanted to be felt. The verses were silly. But my impulses won.

I broke my hands away from those which held me so clammily and began to dance not to the tawdry words but to the Things they were the last tinny echo of, dimensions away.

The words were vulgar. I began leaping away from them.

Danced wilder and wilder, an impulse to open my throat and shout transmuted almost as soon as it started, into a silent vibration which snaked upward.

Hands were on me. I tore them off, and danced on.

A voice said loudly next to me: Now consummate!

I tore off the bandage from my eyes.

And saw Ken struggling to put a contraceptive over his prick.

I pushed him away, laughter pouring out of me like water. And ran laughing away from them all.

Instinct took me to a secret bit of woodland.

Instinct perhaps kept them from finding me.

I was in my silver silence.

Silent.

Learned something.

And knew that to protect it must keep silent.

Sat through the drive home. Thanked them.

Thank you, my friends, for the memory.

And didn't want to see them again.

Knew what I had to do.

# Chapter 21

It is an axiom of life, I've found, that events of any substance seldom take the forms one preconceives for them.

So it was with my rescue.

It came, I think, because I'd stopped chasing after it. I still craved *something* (my partner, my mate?) and for a fleeting moment I had touched it, as a result I now had no idea in what shape, in what size, out of what materials, or through which style, the thing would be formed.

All the forms I'd tried had proved empty.

The night of the woodland faded. For all practical purposes had not happened. Except that it left a memory trace—providing me with more firmness and sense of self than I'd ever possessed before.

So I made a temporizing decision, for practical purposes. I would have to assume that what I sought did not exist in everyday life. It was indeed a sick joke of the romantic fantasists. For if it did exist, then surely in my seen-everything been-everywhere perambulations I would have stumbled on it—this, of course, being a fallacy in which I was hardly alone and in the pursuit of which, this mysterious It, I had sometimes been trodden underfoot in the headlong rush by others even more importunate than I.

I now decided that although whatever-it-was existed, still, as a need in my mind (and I had never found a need in my mind, other than this, which could not find its answer somewhere) then there, for the moment, the matter would have to rest.

I didn't even know what it was I had sacrificed the ease of conventional life to hunt any more. Was it sex? Surely not. Some of it had been good, yet finally left the hunger there. Love? Did I even know what that meant? My perfect mate? I couldn't conceive of him, being imperfect myself. Goodness knew. I didn't.

Without quite framing it in words I decided to take it easy. To try and get my life in some sort of stable, if minor, order, before I became as seedy and sterile as many of the people I had mixed with.

So I slowed down.

I sought out old acquaintances without wanting a thing from them except a few hours' company and the chance to try and see them for what they were—or at least to try and separate out my impression of them from what they were themselves; to see them, if I could, as other than mere extensions of my own desires.

I went to films, usually alone, and watched the stories unfold in a detached and fairly interested way, aware of the story and the characters in it; of the actors as people working at their jobs, more or less well; of myself as both spectator and identifier.

I would go for long walks, watching the traveling of the light and shadow through the trees, seeing the wind move the leaves, and breathing, palpably, the dappled maze of greenish air which sifted through the trees to the level of my eyes.

I was ravished, in spring, by the gloss of a tree's bark, the sheen on the coat of a cat, by the wanton roistering of a blue jay in the garden. A bird walking (because it was such a nice day, perhaps) became the wittiest of jokes.

Everywhere I noticed the essential characteristics of natural things, seeing *treeness, dogness, catness, birdness.* Such qualities were clearer in these creatures than they ever were in humans, myself included. I could have gone into this too far, as I had gone into almost everything else too far, had it not been that now some measure of caution had finally taken root.

Treeness, yes. But that was for trees. I was finally interested in me-ness.

So I merely observed, felt, and let the feeling pass through me.

I dodged encounters with men. In a curious way, after all the tumult and the shouting, I felt virgin again. I had lost my bearings in sexual territory, even in ordinary social encounters with men. First I had blamed men, in the early days in the fog. Then I had blamed myself. Now I simply knew that I was confused, and couldn't rely on any of my earlier assessments. I was new and shy and puzzled. Had I ever really known anything about that territory? I decided that probably no one else knew much either.

One of the reasons I dodged male encounters was the fact that my responses were awry. Although I found I could no longer respond if a man approached me on a sexual basis (for I could write any of the scripts in advance) this limitation was only psychological: my body responded treacherously, without regard to the social context. On one occasion, for example, having coffee with a group of colleagues, one of them put his arm around me and started pantomiming lust. To my embarrassment, my body leapt with desire in the instant, though *he* was feeling none. At the same time, my mind coolly analyzed the man, his characteristics, his potential sexual needs, and recognized the game as a game which called for a cool or funny light-response I could not make.

I knew all the forms, but felt myself without substance.

So I decided to keep myself quiet, until I could have a simple relationship. Or more—not to estimate in advance what I would do. And if there were no more beds, and no more tenderness, and no more thrilled swoonings (and what I discounted largely was the great amount of sheer animal pleasure I had taken over the years) then at last there would be no more pain either, and I would be left with my remarkable and riotous memories.

After the sweeping cycles of my amorous life, which had searched over the foglands in huge radar-scanning arcs, I came to the same conclusions I could have adduced before I bolted toward Ben and married him: take it easy, wait and see, respond to what comes your way, don't demand of others what you cannot manage yourself, do your best, don't act on importunate wants, get on with it.

Dull stuff for thrill seekers.

But I'd had enough thrills.

In this mood I noticed, almost absently, that the very people who would have excited my imagination before, because of some oddity, or freakiness, or wit, or brilliance; because of some dominant edge of their personality which sought to command attention, and around which the remainder of their personalities were structured, were the ones who engaged me least. I came, instead, to respect the ones with no edges of that kind showing; who could not be grasped, in that way. I was a past mistress at taking such knobs and twisting them, wrenching them, manipulating them; dancing like a Fascinator in front of them.

But these others offered no purchase. They were very often their own people; their surfaces impermeable; they offered the behavior necessary for the present encounter and the base from which the behavior came was private. Their own business.

In the fog, lacking any real perceptions or any

agreed conventions; lacking, moreover, real courtesy; we institutionalized into ritual conversations our depressions and excitements, and the light and dark of our intimate lives, handing them over across the coffee cups, making gifts of them in strange beds. But now I saw that what I had considered made for a "dull" personality did not necessarily add up to a less worthwhile person.

Among the decent and unflamboyant and silent were a few who could reach me now in a way that had been impossible before, who knew things I had been blind to as ways of structuring and disciplining the mind: how to put together a piece of furniture, how to grow roses, how to make shoes. Form them I began to learn about such ordinary matters I'd missed out on, realizing, at last, that the things themselves mattered less than the qualities exercised while doing them. Consideration, thoughtfulness, and interest in others were not qualities to be found—except mocked up for a motive—in the fog.

Finally the glitter had faded through surfeit.

Christ, I'd nearly had to choke on it before I gave up. I know that round about this time some of my former friends thought I was a goner. I heard rumors that I'd died in childbirth, and others that I was in a mental institution.

Poor old Annie. She was a good kid, really.

In fact, all that had happened was that I was sitting it out, cautiously, on a small islet of calm and comparatively clean air, very close to the light.

I'd stopped dancing now.

But the night in the woods, and the droplets of light, my long-lost light-beads, which had begun to collect again, my specks of mercury and pearl, had caused me to wonder. . . .

To rack my brains. . . .

To remember something I had once known.

## Chapter 22

Now I was working steadily again, having taken a job from an old friend and lover, an American photographer. I did dullish portrait work in his studio, while he skimmed the world, from Vietnam to the latest riot spots, freezing the action and inoculating the world daily at breakfast time, part of the numbing daily dose of horror, to be swallowed with tea and toast.

But to me, the world was beginning to look different. Lighter. I'd burned off the worst of my cloudiness through dancing.

And now I was in a somewhat investigative mood. Once more I was being quite chaste. But sex, and its puzzlements, still exercised me. I started collecting information; confirming hunches.

Sometimes I would put on a blonde wig and walk down the street, noticing that the men who stared and made eyes at me, were not the same ones who ogled me down the same street when I was brunette. Then I would alter my style of dress, and notice how a man who talked to me seriously, as a chap, almost, would be unable to suppress a quite different range of responses, like feeling me up quite often, if I wore a lowcut sexy dress. Over the months I lost a lot of weight, for I was hardly eating now, and I noticed yet again how the approaches changed: the ones who wanted to put their heads on my ample bosom, ha ha, did not feel so inclined when I was a fashionable wraith. But plenty of others buzzed my way, fruitily. If I was animated, I would attract the attention of one type; if I were secretively silent, of another.

And most interesting of all, if I overreacted to their signals and approaches, there were two different results. Either they would run away frightened, or else they would imagine they had fallen in love.

I became adept at pushing buttons. Before I had known only in theory how much we were all creatures responding to triggers, but it had never really penetrated to me how thoroughgoing this was. Now I was getting to know the taste of this automatism, to be able to predict it, and sometimes—for a moment—to separate out my emotions and desires from the moves made toward me —while remaining as little or as well disposed to the person as I had been before the analysis.

With interest, I noticed that I, too, as much as —perhaps more than—the others, was buffeted by whatever wind or suggestion or stimulus button was activated.

It was in this mood of experimental curiosity

that I accepted a dinner invitation—party invitation, rather—from Ken. It was his parents' silver wedding anniversary, his girlfriend had let him down, if I wasn't doing anything perhaps I'd like to come.

I went, neutrally enough.

There were a couple of dozen people there, many of them members of the family. We drank beer and sang bawdy songs and toasted the couple who then left, with surprising skittishness, like a newlywed couple on a second honeymoon. We watched them go, they were driving to a hotel for the night on the outskirts of Brighton, and then returned inside, to drink, to dance, and to talk.

It was while I was dancing that I became aware of someone watching me. A businessman, George Marshall, to whom I'd been introduced a little earlier. His eyes had bothered me, but then he'd moved out of range, and I'd been talking and listening, and watching, which was my latest game, and had forgotten him.

Now I saw him again. His eyes were, somehow, endless. Though they were not obviously staring out, if one caught his gaze one was held; one could not gaze back *into* his eyes, they held you at their surface, but somehow deliberately; there was no wobble, only steadiness. He started up a turmoil within me which I thought I had finished with forever. When I stopped dancing I went and sat by his side, like a kid, and stuck with him for the rest of the evening.

There was something about him which so attracted me that I simply wanted to be near it.

Over my years in England I had fallen victim

to the constraint which affects many women who are unsure of themselves, or who have been too hurt. It goes like this: "Never show a man you like him."

The devious lengths I, and friends like me, could go to simply to appear unaffected by someone who had caught one's attention were the result, I think, of the English technique of freezing women into postures which they named importunate, or predatory, or voracious. After one's early twenties one had to be careful how one showed one's interest, for if the man didn't fancy you in return you were often made to feel graceless, at best; or at worst like a whore.

There were, though, a repertoire of tricks—insinuation, invitation, net-casting for shared activity, through which, without ever raising the miserable subject of sex, one could express, by analogy in shared interest, one's desire to see more of someone.

I was adept at this.

But when the party ended, and George Marshall got his coat to leave, I hated the thought that I might never see him again, and asked him directly if I could get in touch with him and ask him for dinner one night soon.

"Yes, that would be very nice," he said, lightly, politely, as I still stared at him, addled. He regarded me in return, penetrating and neutral, friendly but somehow unshakeable, utterly disturbing in a way I couldn't fathom.

That was the beginning.

Next day at work my state of mind was akin to

the girl I had been before I met Arne. My head was full of George. He was my preferred blonde, once again, very tall, with an almost military bearing. I had never met an Englishman who had looked at me quite that way. I doubted, in fact, if I had met many capable of such depth and open regarding.

Paradoxical, that after my scorn and contempt and harsh treatment and pain, given and got at the hands of the English, it should have been an Englishman who acted as courier on my journey from the fog!

Casually, I questioned Ken about George. Ken, it became clear, didn't think he was in any way remarkable, though he liked him immensely. He could tell me little.

"Mum's known him for years. So have I, but I couldn't tell you much about him."

"What does he do?"

"Business of some sort."

"Do you know what sort?"

"Christ, why are you suddenly so interested?"

He looked at me speculating.

Normally I would have concealed my interest. But not now. "I'd like to see him again. He seemed really nice."

"Yes he is. Very square though, he's in some kind of trading."

"Does he have a girlfriend?"

"Don't know. Don't know much about him. I know he's active in that department. At least I mean he was engaged once, I think."

It was infuriatingly vague.

"What happened, do you know, Ken?"

"No. Don't really know much about him. I just remembered him helping out over the years, mending my bicycle for me when I was a kid; later he taught me to drive. That sort of thing."

With a careful sense of timing, I waited ten days, then phoned him. Yes, he would like to come for dinner. In about three weeks' time.

The days passed. The night of the dinner became the single living event looming in my life, the rest passing in shadow. I could have been fifteen again. I made the meal hundreds of times in my head; bought the ingredients in dozens of different shops; cooked it in my imagination with attentive care. I changed the menu a dozen times; dressed and redressed myself in different clothes which I saw in the shops I passed as I roamed round town.

When the day finally came, I took off work, cleaned the flat till it shone, shopped, cooked, scented and oiled myself in a fragrant bath, performed the rituals which normally I scorned.

I lit candles in the room we would eat in, and dressed myself in a long green summer gown, showing my figure softly at my breasts and ankles, which were my good points, and cut low over my back and shoulders, which were excellent. I was acting mindlessly; playing out some dimly sensed scene of courtesan or hetaira which had got mixed up with the *Vogue* ads for perfume, or Dubonnet. I transformed my poky little attic into a time-capsule, sexpool, with incense in the air, and spring flowers, bluebells and blossoms, in the vases.

I sensed it didn't really matter if I met in this setting or workaday, in my jeans. But training won: I wanted to present, as it were, a high-profile image.

After what I'd been through in the previous years, the optimism for the Beautiful Experience still was not washed out.

I'm not sure what I expected, really.

In any case, it was like nothing I'd known before.

# Chapter 23

I actually met someone, for once.

Where I had been in the woodland, in the silver, another now joined me.

When George arrived he looked around him appreciatively, paying no compliments but noting the state of affairs. My blatant preparations for romance didn't seem to make him uncomfortable; didn't seem to affect him at all. He started speaking to *me*, bypassing the environment, until I, too, got the carefully prepared environment into perspective. After all, people can meet anywhere.

We chatted in the little kitchen while I did the last of the cooking, and after we'd drunk a little wine and eaten just a little food I absolutely relaxed. I didn't care what happened for the rest of the evening, if anything. I was contented in this person's company, listening to what he was saying, following the direction where his thoughts led with my own attending thoughts. He talked quietly, but as if he knew that what he said was worth saying, and I listened fascinated, almost hypnotized, as he told me about the stalking and hunting he had done as a boy in the north of England.

Absorbed, I never took my eyes off him. It seemed as if he was telling me about far more than the activities he described.

*As if somehow the whole forest, and the creatures in it, hunters and hunted, and the care each took, and the relationships between them, and the direction of the wind, and the understanding between man and animal, and the life and growth of the eternal forest through which the creatures moved, man, dog, and prey, and what man could learn, and dog could learn, and fox or rabbit or bird could learn, were purer reflections of a world I should have learned, and had not done so, in spite of being every one of those creatures myself, in spite of having been both hunter and quarry.*

Somehow, as he talked, he lit possibilities for life which had been dormant.

I was happier than I had been for years that night.

When he rose to go, I panicked.

I rebounded into all my old ways, bringing out toys to entrance him, and whimsies to please him, and pert tricks to tempt him, and all the magnificence and desirability I could find in the remnants of my Pandora's box to delay him.

And he stayed.

But he stayed because he chose to.

He told me later that he hadn't realized, until that last desperate bid, disguised and tricked out as it was, that I was shouting for help.

He actually *saw*.

And knew he might be able to help.

The permissive period has introduced us to many ways of making love, and believe me, I've known a fair share of them, from the feather on the end of the contraceptive sheath to the careful programming of positions, to the teasing nerve-concussion of more than one person exciting me at once. Some of it was delicious, remarkable, or funny. Some was boring. But the effect of such things was merely to introduce me to a wider range of producing effects of greater or less intensity.

Just about all of it was recreational and gymnastic. But I was looking for something, so I thought, closer to the sacramental.

Certainly, all my experience gave me no more understanding of the nature of the sexual act and the nature of my own needs than I had gained by the time Jeffrey had done me in.

But now, without tricks or fancy style, but because he was clear-sighted and appreciated my state, I learned something—in or out of bed was not germane—for the first time for years.

*I learned, because George Marshall was not a not-person.*

Somehow, after all these years, he released in me the glimmerings of understanding. I lost my other virginity—my psychological virginity, that sealed aspect of myself which had eluded me for so long; not so that I got out of the bed in any way noticeably different, but so that I knew—to actualize later—that dimly, but deep, I had been rejoined to myself.

## Chapter 24

There are so many different things here which we, in our poverty, give just one name.

Sex is different each time one performs it. It is a new time, a new place, a new person, a potential for different exchange, on each occasion. Another context; a different mood; a newly aspected intention; an altered state.

In the years that followed, I realized that there are levels in everything: sexual behavior, understanding, affection, commitment, thoughtfulness, concern. I learned, too, that whether the communication takes place physically, through what we call sex, or in any of the other channels through which we communicate, us silly people, only one things matters: the depth of one's understanding, and the cleanness of intention; thought for the other, and abandonment—not orgiastic abandonment, except as a technique for the other kind: the letting fall of the preconceptions and attitudes one is normally clothed in.

What I had thought was possible, in love-making, was, after all, possible. My birthright of ancient knowledge in such matters was finally called out.

I cannot tell you how he did it.

And I will not tell you what we did.

In any case, one could not accurately transmit it on the page. Even if one wished to, there are things one should be careful not to attempt. I can only say that as I was pushed further in my capacity, further beyond my waking mind, I *remembered* something. I reached a point, not only physical but also psychological, where I rejoined with a part of my stable sense of self that I had left behind in childhood, and had touched again in the woodland.

And when that was achieved I knew that what we tout or tell about sex, or love, is false.

The no-holds-barred portrait
of Janis Joplin

# Going Down
# with Janis

by Peggy Caserta
as told to Dan Knapp

**MAKING IT** in the rock world, from four buck
coffee house gigs to fifty grand one-nighters
and million dollar albums

**MAKING IT** with drugs, grass and speed and
acid and smack

**MAKING IT** with men, from fellow stars like
Kris Kristofferson to the beautiful blond boys
picked up on the street

**MAKING IT** with women, from the black girl
who was her first female lover to the swarm of
feminine admirers

*And at her side Peggy Caserta, who shared Janis Joplin's
meteorlike flight through the show-biz heavens, and her
plunge into hell ...*

**GOING DOWN WITH JANIS**

**A Dell Book $1.50**

If you cannot obtain copies of this title at your local bookseller, just send
the price (plus 25c per copy for handling and postage) to Dell Books, Post
Office Box 1000, Pinebrook, N. J. 07058.

The big new novel of a girl . . .
an affair . . . an obsession

# Ellie

## HERBERT KASTLE

**Author of *Miami Golden Boy* and *Millionaires***

Ellie was a salesgirl, a cute blonde number, twenty very sexy and uninhibited years old.

Nick was a toy manufacturer, sophisticated, divorced, more than twice Ellie's age.

As far as Nick was concerned, she would be just another chick in a long string of conquests.

Then they went to bed together, and nothing had ever equalled it. He had to have her completely, constantly, exclusively, and there was nothing he wouldn't do—nothing at all—to make sure that she was his and only his.

**A Dell Book $1.50**

If you cannot obtain copies of this title from your local bookseller, just send the price (plus 25¢ per copy for handling and postage) to Dell Books, Post Office Box 1000, Pinebrook, N. J. 07058.

# HOW MANY OF THESE DELL BESTSELLERS HAVE YOU READ?

## Fiction

1. **THE TAKING OF PELHAM ONE TWO THREE**
   by John Godey                                         $1.75
2. **ELLIE** by Herbert Kastle                           $1.50
3. **PEOPLE WILL ALWAYS BE KIND** by Wilfrid Sheed  $1.50
4. **SHOOT** by Douglas Fairbairn                        $1.50
5. **A DAY NO PIGS WOULD DIE**
   by Robert Newton Peck                                 $1.25
6. **ELEPHANTS CAN REMEMBER** by Agatha Christie  $1.25
7. **TREVAYNE** by Jonathan Ryder                        $1.50
8. **DUST ON THE SEA** by Edward L. Beach                $1.75
9. **THE CAR THIEF** by Theodore Weesner                 $1.50
10. **THE MORNING AFTER** by Jack B. Weiner              $1.50

## Non-fiction

1. **AN UNTOLD STORY**
   by Elliott Roosevelt and James Brough                 $1.75
2. **QUEEN VICTORIA** by Cecil Woodham-Smith            $1.75
3. **GOING DOWN WITH JANIS**
   by Peggy Caserta & Dan Knapp                          $1.50
4. **SOLDIER** by Anthony B. Herbert                     $1.75
5. **THE WATER IS WIDE** by Pat Conroy                   $1.50
6. **THE GREAT EXECUTIVE DREAM** by Robert Heller  $1.75
7. **TARGET BLUE** by Robert Daley                       $1.75
8. **MEAT ON THE HOOF** by Gary Shaw                     $1.50
9. **MARJOE** by Stephen S. Gaines                       $1.50
10. **LUCY** by Joe Morella & Edward Z. Epstein          $1.50

If you cannot obtain copies of these titles from your local bookseller, just send the price (plus 25¢ per copy for handling and postage) to Dell Books, Post Office Box 1000, Pinebrook, N. J. 07058.